DATE DUE

ABOUT THE BOOK

Ann Stepp's comprehensive study of the uses and misuses of nuclear energy was undertaken from her deep sense of commitment that people be able to express themselves intelligently as new and increased uses of atomic power take root in our communities.

Contrasting peaceful applications of nuclear energy to its devastating wartime power, the author shows how it helps control crops, minimize disease in cattle, and preserve food. She gives us a detailed look at its medical applications and at its ability to generate power for electricity and travel. And she gives us a look into future uses planned by scientists for restructuring the earth—excavating for dams and canals, creating new harbors, moving vast tonnages of earth to uncover rich mineral deposits. But she issues warnings, too, in her in-depth discussion of the problems of disposing of radioactive waste materials.

An important book for an important era in the earth's history, *The Story of Radioactivity* is illustrated with photos and drawings, and contains a reading list, a glossary and an index.

THE STORY OF

Radioactivity

THE STORY OF

Radioactivity

by

ANN STEPP

Illustrated by James Barry

HARVEY HOUSE, INC.
Publishers
Irvington-on-Hudson, N.Y. 10533

Cover photograph Aerojet-General Corporation

Contents

Preface

This book is about radioactivity. In the pages which follow you will learn how man unlocked the key to atomic energy. As the story of radioactivity unfolds, you will discover how an atom can be split, what happens when it does split, and how the atom's controlled power is being used to benefit man.

Atomic energy is a subject that every person is obligated to understand. The fundamental ideas of atomic energy are not difficult. Words such as "fission," "fusion," "isotope," "alpha ray," and "chain reaction" should not frighten you. The aim of this book is to give the reader a basic understanding of atomic energy so that he can involve himself in intelligent participation in a world that will become more and more dominated by the atom.

The military atom displayed its frightening destructive power in the bombs which were dropped on Japan in 1945 to end World War II. It is necessary that people not only understand the sinister threat in the atom's destructive power, but also know its creative power, which can be used to give all mankind a better life. Humanity must always come first. The application of atomic knowledge must be for the goals of human comfort, happiness, and achievement.

It is hoped that *The Story of Radioactivity* will open new vistas for young, eager minds. Nuclear research today is varied and rewarding. The atom is now part of the past and of the present. The future is always before us. And the future and its exciting possibilities in nuclear work belongs to you—the young men and young women of the world.

A number of people have helped to make this book possible. Grateful acknowledgment is extended for the many practical suggestions received from the following authorities: Walter C. Ralston, M.D.; William E. Boyer, Associate Professor of Physics, Chapman College; Vance Gritton, Assistant Professor of Chemistry, Chapman College; and Frank W. Reeder, Information Officer, Salt Lake City, Utah Civil Defense. Appreciation is also due to those organizations, especially the Atomic Energy Commission, who graciously furnished photographs for the book. Finally, deep gratitude is extended to Joe Lee Ferguson, Jr. for his many helpful suggestions.

ANN STEPP

To my mother,
And in memory of my father,
William W. Stepp, Sr.

Hydrogen bomb explosion at the Atomic Energy Commission's Pacific Proving Grounds in the Marshall Islands.

1

Public Awakening

ON MARCH 1, 1954, A BRILLIANT FLASH covered the skies, a large shudder shook the earth, a great roar was released, and a huge mushroom-shaped cloud stood high in the skies.

Approximately six hours later, white flaky particles began to fall on the sixty-four Marshallese natives living at the southeast corner of the island of Rongelap. The Marshall Islands are north of the equator in the western Pacific Ocean and are in two parallel chains approximately 100 miles apart.

Some of the islanders described the particles as looking like snow. But the particles were not moist and cold as is snow.

A nuclear weapon of about fifteen megatons had been exploded at a test site on another Marshall Island, Bikini. According to plan, the fallout was supposed to have dropped over the ocean where there were no people. But because of an unexpected shift in wind direction, the fallout produced by the bomb fell 100 miles east of Bikini on Rongelap Island.

Fallout particles are not always light in color as were those that fell on Rongelap Island. The particles can be light or dark, and they may or may not be seen.

Islanders Ignore Fallout

The islanders, unaware of the dangers of fallout, ignored the flaky particles. For the next two days they continued to live as they always had. They drank water from their open cisterns; they cooked their food outdoors; they walked barefoot in the radioactive dust.

As soon as the United States learned what had happened, the island was evacuated. The sixty-four villagers were taken to Kwajalein Island, 300 miles away. An American medical team was immediately flown from Washington, D.C., to Kwajalein.

A few of the islanders became nauseated and vomited. The other villagers showed no immediate outward symptoms as a result of the exposure to the radiation. By March 11, 1954, ten days after the islanders had been exposed, certain areas of their bodies appeared to have been severely sunburned, and the islanders complained of itching and burning sensations.

Those burns appeared only on the body parts which had not been covered with clothing and which had been sweaty and sticky. The front of the neck, the armpits, the folds of the elbows, and the bare feet were the areas that the flaky particles touched and directly exposed. The skin peeled from these areas, and most of the bodies eventually healed completely.

Approximately a month after the fallout exposure, some of the islanders suffered hair loss. The hair eventually grew back, however, and none suffered permanent baldness.

Exposure to radioactivity is measured by the "roentgen." The Rongelap people received body doses of about 175 roentgens

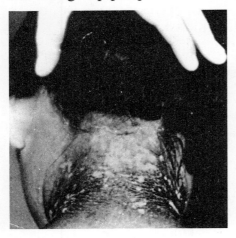

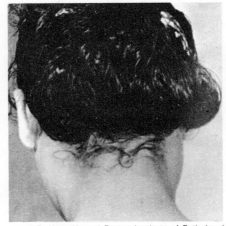

U.S. Navy (Armed Forces Institute of Pathology)

Rongelap women 28 days after exposure to beta particles from fallout.

Rongelap woman after her recovery from beta burns.

in their two days of living with fallout. The roentgen, sometimes abbreviated to r, is a standard unit used to designate the quantity of absorbed energy from radiation.

Radiation Sickness

Usually a dosage of 200 r or less produces no serious disabling symptoms. If exposed to 200 to 400 r, a person will experience radiation sickness. As a result of radiation sickness, a person may become nauseated, lose his appetite, feel fatigued, have diarrhea, develop bleeding of the mouth, have a drop in his count of white blood cells, and lose his hair. Because of the drop in the white blood cells, victims have a tendency to develop infections. In spite of blood transfusions and injections of antibiotics for infections, an exposure of 500 roentgens or more is likely to be fatal.

The fundamental effect of radiation on any living organism is the destruction of the cells of the body. This destruction of the cells is believed to be caused by the radiation destroying the chemical bonds of the cells. Since the nucleus controls all of the cell's activities, radiation affects the entire cell if the nucleus becomes abnormal.

Radiation can be more dangerous in the body than outside it. No precautions were taken by the islanders to prevent internal exposure of their bodies to radiation. The food they ate, the water they drank, and the air they breathed were contaminated with radioactive particles.

The Rongelap villagers on Kwajalein were eventually returned to their own island. Each year since then, a medical team visits them to check for possible aftereffects.

In 1961, seven years later, the level of the red blood cells count for the islanders was still lower than normal, which suggested that the bone marrow injuries had not healed completely. There was also an indication that the children who were babies at the time of the exposure had retarded bone growth.

15

In 1968 some of the islanders had to be flown to Boston, Massachusetts, to have growths removed from their thyroid glands. This abnormality has developed in approximately ninety percent of the children. Only the passage of time will reveal other symptoms that may arise out of this radiation exposure.

The villagers of Rongelap Island could have had a worse fate. If the village had been located on the northern tip of the island, those people would have been exposed to radiation dosages of over 1,000 roentgens. This dosage would have been sure death for everyone in less than a month.

An Unlucky Crew

At the same time, a Japanese fishing boat, the "Lucky Dragon," was approximately 120 miles away from the explosion. A danger area had been determined by the Americans before the test. The boat, like Rongelap Island, was supposed to have been well outside of this area. Due to the wind change, the boat was smothered with radioactive dust.

That night some of the fishermen became nauseated. They felt as if they were seasick. This condition baffled them, for the sea was calm. There was no apparent reason for the fishermen to be seasick.

Parts of their skin became red and began to hurt where the radioactive dust had stuck to their bodies. After a few days had passed, some of the fishermen began to lose their hair.

On March 14, 1954, the twenty-three fishermen reached their home port of Yaizu. By this time, all the men were sick. They had no idea why they were ill, but they did realize that their troubles started after the white flakes covered their boat. The unlucky crew of the "Lucky Dragon" was taken immediately to the hospital. One man, the wireless operator, died a few months later.

The nuclear explosion that affected the Marshall islanders and the "Lucky Dragon" boat crew certainly made the world even more aware of the dangers of radiation.

16

2

Structure of the Atom

JUST WHAT IS RADIATION? How can exposure to fallout cause severe burns and loss of hair? What are these dangerous rays that cannot be felt, seen, smelled, or tasted? What are these invisible rays that endanger the air we breathe, the food we eat, and the water we drink? Are these rays always dangerous to man?

To understand radioactivity, one must understand the structure of the atom. The basic particles that make up the center of the atom also make up these invisible rays.

Every time you look at a chair or at an ice-cream cone or at a large building, you are seeing atoms—masses and masses of atoms. The billions of atoms are clinging together to give the object its shape, its color, and its basic characteristics.

The atom is inconceivably small—even to the wildest imagination. There are thirty billion times more atoms in the head of a pin than there are people on the earth. Even though atoms are so minute, scientists know many things about their structure.

Protons, Electrons, and Neutrons

Three types of particles—electrons, protons, and neutrons —are the basic units of an atom. Electrons whiz in orbits around the core of the atom. This core is called its nucleus, and it is in the center of the atom. Protons and neutrons are located in the nucleus.

Protons carry a positive electrical charge. The number of protons in the atom determines the kind of atom. All of us have seen the red-orange metal, copper, and the silvery metal, zinc.

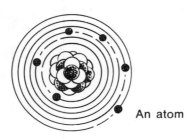

An atom

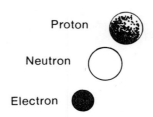

Proton

Neutron

Electron

A zinc atom is different from a copper atom because it contains thirty protons, whereas copper contains only twenty-nine. If a proton were knocked from the nucleus of the zinc atom, it would no longer be zinc. It would then become copper.

For every proton in the nucleus, there is an electron whizzing at a tremendous speed in an orbit outside the nucleus. All electrons have a negative electrical charge, the opposite of the proton.

Most atoms are basically neutral in electrical charge. If an atom contains six protons (positive charges), then how many electrons must the atom have whirling in its orbits in order for it to be neutral? Six is the correct answer. There must be six negative charges to neutralize the six positive charges.

In all the atoms, except the hydrogen-1 atom, there are also neutrons in the nucleus. The neutron has no electrical charge. It is said to be electrically neutral. It contains neither a negative charge nor a positive charge.

The Size of the Atom

If you could see an atom, what would it look like? Would a copper atom look like a shiny copper-colored ball? Would a zinc atom look like a silver ball? No. It would look very empty. There would be mostly . . . .

empty space

To visualize the atom, let us enlarge the nucleus to the size of a pea and construct an atom. The space between the nucleus and the electrons would be about one mile. Even though the atom is very, very small, it is truly a giant when compared to the protons, neutrons, and electrons of which it is composed.

18

Amazingly enough, one of the most important facts about the atom is its weight! The proton is 1,840 times heavier than the electron. As you can imagine, the proton weighs very, very little. It takes about 260,000,000,000,000,000,000,000,000 protons to make one pound. This is a very large number, and it would be ridiculous to use such a number. Instead, scientists decided to let the weight of a proton be represented by the number one. The neutron is approximately the same weight as the proton, and it has also been assigned the weight of one. Because the electron is so light, compared to the proton and the neutron, in some cases it has been assigned the weight of zero.

Since the protons and the neutrons are the particles that have most of the weight, 99.9 percent of the atom's weight is found in its tiny nucleus. The total number of protons and neutrons in the nucleus determines the atomic mass number of the atom. Helium has two protons and two neutrons in its nucleus; therefore, its atomic mass number is four. Helium could also be referred to as helium-4.

Atom of hydrogen-1

Isotopes

The only atoms that do not contain a neutron are the atoms of hydrogen-1. The hydrogen-1 nuclei contain only one proton. Hydrogen-1 is the lightest element. Some hydrogen atoms contain one proton and one neutron and are called hydrogen-2 atoms. Some hydrogen atoms contain one proton and two neutrons and are called hydrogen-3 atoms. When atoms of one element differ from each other only in the number of neutrons in their respective nuclei, they are called isotopes. Hydrogen-1, hydrogen-2, and hydrogen-3 are called hydrogen isotopes.

Atoms with the same number of protons may differ in the number of neutrons they contain. Isotopes of the same element are identified by their atomic mass number, which is written after the element.

Every kind of atom except hydrogen has more than one proton and one electron. As atoms become heavier, they contain more protons, neutrons, and electrons.

Nuclear Glue

Atoms heavier than hydrogen could not exist if they contained protons and electrons only. The positive charges on two or more protons in a nucleus would cause the protons to repel each other, and the nucleus would fly apart. Neutrons act as "nuclear glue," which holds the protons together. The neutron has no electrical charge, but when it is near a proton, there exists a strong attraction between them. It is this attraction that holds the protons and neutrons tightly in the nucleus.

Each atom must contain a certain number of neutrons so that the protons will not fly out of the nucleus. Scientists have found that calcium is the heaviest atom that will hold equal numbers of protons and neutrons. The normal isotope of calcium has twenty electrons whirling in its orbit. The atoms of all heavier elements contain more neutrons than protons.

There are three common isotopes of lead. In these three various isotopes, 124, 125 and 126 neutrons hold the 82 protons in the nucleus. Remember, it is the number of protons that determines the kind of atom.

Bismuth has 83 protons and 126 neutrons in its nucleus. There are heavier atoms than lead and bismuth. But the atoms which have more than 83 protons in their nuclei become unstable. An "unstable" nucleus is one that will eventually disintegrate, or decay. When there are more than 83 protons in a nucleus, extra neutrons cannot supply the necessary "glue" to hold the nucleus together.

3

Radiation

SUBSTANCES MADE OF ATOMS that have unstable nuclei are called "radioactive." Radium and uranium are radioactive substances.

In an atom which is radioactive, the nucleus will eventually break down. The nucleus is in a state of change, and some of the basic particles which make up the nucleus are sent flying out of the atom. The particle or particles ejected from the nucleus possess kinetic energy; energy of motion.

The nuclei of all radioactive atoms sooner or later disintegrate of their own accord. Radioactivity is an automatic process which man cannot speed up or slow down.

The Fission Process

The volume of the nucleus is very small compared to the total volume of the atom. A large concentration of energy is needed to hold the protons and the neutrons firmly in place. The very existence of radioactive elements in nature, such as uranium, shows that the atomic nuclei must contain concentrated energy in order to eject such powerful rays. This knowledge has paved the way for the fission process.

In the case of the large atoms, the impact of a particle upon the nucleus loosens its binding force. This causes the nucleus to fly apart into fragments which leave the scene at such high speeds that each fragment possesses tremendous energy. This process is called fission.

What happens within the nucleus to cause it to split? Normally, the particles in the nucleus of the atom stick close together. This attraction of the neutrons and protons results in a

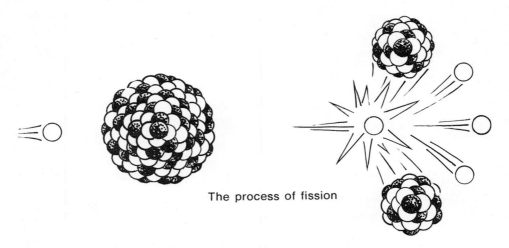

The process of fission

round shape. When the nucleus is undisturbed, there is an even distribution of protons throughout the nucleus. If an extra neutron is absorbed, it adds excess energy and excites particles of the nucleus. The distribution of the protons becomes uneven, and the shape of the nucleus becomes slightly elongated. The mutual repulsion of the protons leads to positive charges on the ends. The repelling forces finally win out, and the nucleus splits apart.

Nuclei do not always split into exactly the same pieces. This fact is really not surprising. After all, two cups will not break into the same pieces when they are dropped on the floor.

The major distinction between fission and radioactivity is that in radioactivity the nucleus is not split into nuclear fragments as in fission; rather, it simply ejects a small part of its nucleus.

Uranium Fission

When the nuclei of uranium atoms are split, the fragments are nuclei of lighter atoms which pick up electrons to form neutral atoms of common elements. Although the nuclei do not always form the same elements, scientists have found that usually the uranium nucleus splits and forms the lighter elements, barium and krypton.

22

During the splitting of the nucleus, one or more neutrons fly off into space. If one of these neutrons hits another uranium nucleus, it will cause that nucleus to shatter. Each time a nucleus splits, more neutrons are included in the release which hits more nuclei. This is called a "chain reaction," and is the principle used in the atomic bomb and atomic power plants.

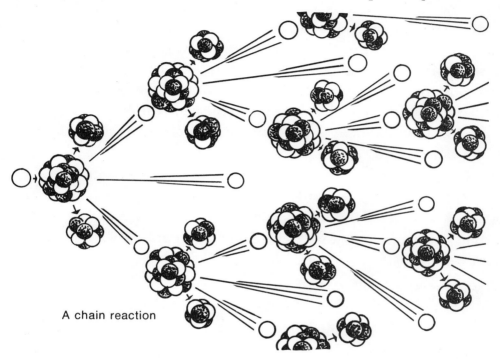

A chain reaction

Each time a nucleus splits or emits a particle, a small part of the energy concentrated in the nucleus is also emitted in the form of radiation. Since the number of protons determines the kind of atom, if one or more protons are included in this release from the nucleus, the atom becomes a complete new atom.

All radioactive elements disintegrate into a succession of other elements; most of these are radioactive and thus temporary. After successive decays, the nucleus is gradually reduced to that of stable lead. Stable lead is not radioactive and does not continue to decay. Very few atoms lighter than lead are naturally radioactive.

As the nucleus breaks down, there are three kinds of rays that may be released. These rays have been named after the first three letters of the Greek alphabet—alpha, beta, and gamma. What are these three rays, and how do they differ?

The Alpha Ray

The alpha ray is composed of two protons and two neutrons. The helium atom has in its nucleus two protons and two neutrons. Therefore, the alpha ray is simply a helium nucleus moving at a high speed. Because it contains two protons, it has two positive charges. It has the atomic mass number of four because it has a total of four protons and neutrons.

An alpha particle is shot out of a nucleus at about 20,000 miles per second. This is a speed hundreds of times faster than our fastest jet planes. Because it collides with many atoms in the air, an alpha particle can travel only a short distance before it loses its energy. A thin sheet of paper or even two inches of air usually stops an alpha particle. Your skin can keep alpha particles from passing into your body.

The Beta Ray

Beta rays are streams of electrons that move at about nine-tenths the speed of light. Light travels 186,000 miles per second. A beta particle is much more penetrating than the comparatively slower-moving alpha particles. The beta ray has little mass compared to the alpha ray, but it does have much greater speed. Even though the beta ray is traveling much faster than the alpha particles, most beta particles can be stopped by thin sheets of metal, clothing, or several sheets of paper, because electrons are so light.

The beta particle is emitted from the nucleus. As you know, there are no electrons in the nucleus, only protons and neutrons. Where, then, does the electron come from? The beta particle is formed when the neutron breaks down into two pieces and becomes an electron and a proton. The electron is shot from the nucleus while the proton remains. The nucleus now has one less neutron and has added a proton. By ejecting an electron, the neutron has changed to a proton. A new atom has been formed because the number of protons has been increased by one.

Since protons and neutrons make up the alpha ray, and electrons make up the beta ray, the alpha and beta rays should more appropriately be referred to as alpha and beta particles, while gamma rays are actually energy rays.

The Gamma Ray

The third type of ray, the gamma ray, is a form of electromagnetic radiation. Radio waves, light, and x-rays are other examples of electromagnetic radiation. Gamma rays are similar to light but are much more energetic.

The gamma ray is usually emitted when an alpha or a beta particle is ejected from the nucleus. When the particles that remain in the nucleus rearrange themselves to a new position, a gamma ray is given off. This extremely energetic radiation is traveling at the speed of light. The gamma ray is the most damaging and penetrating form of radiation to our bodies.

Gamma rays are similar to x-rays. You have probably had your teeth and chest x-rayed. X-rays are very energetic forms of energy and pass through human flesh with ease. Gamma rays penetrate matter even more easily than do x-rays. Because of this ability, they are much more dangerous. They pass through your body as if it were not there. This is dangerous, because in their "dash" through your body, gamma rays are bound to strike and affect some of the atoms that make up your cells.

Gamma rays penetrate thin sheets of most materials. Scientists have found that an inch or more of lead or of iron, eight inches of heavy concrete, or three feet of sod will stop gamma radiation.

High-Speed Neutrons

Another form of radiation that man must protect himself from are the high-speed neutrons which are sent flying at the time of an uncontrolled nuclear reaction or a nuclear explosion. These neutrons can penetrate most solid walls and therefore can be dangerous to living cells. There is no special name assigned to these fast neutrons as there is to the alpha, beta, and gamma rays.

Each radioactive element emits a certain ray and/or rays. Some emit alpha particles; others emit beta particles; others emit beta particles and gamma rays; others emit alpha particles and gamma rays; and others emit alpha and beta particles.

Decay of Radium

When radium disintegrates, it is said to decay. What happens to the radium that decayed? Remember that all elements which have more than 82 protons (lead) or 83 protons (bismuth) are radioactive. As the original radium atoms (88 protons) emit their alpha rays, they change into atoms of another unstable element, radon. As long as unstable isotopes are formed, they will continue to go through the decaying process by emitting alpha or beta rays until a stable isotope of lead or a stable isotope of some other element is formed. When this happens, the decay process stops.

This series of atoms formed as radium decays is called the radioactive transformation series of radium. Transformation means that a new atom is formed with each emission.

In the chart below are the changes that take place from radium to the formation of stable lead. The number to the left and at the top of the element is the atomic number (number of protons the atom contains). The number on the right and below the element is the atomic mass number (number of protons and neutrons the atom contains). The emission of an

26

alpha particle results in the loss of two protons and two neutrons.

The emission of a beta particle results in the loss of a neutron. A negative electron is shot out of the nucleus, and a positive proton replaces the neutron. Very little mass is lost in the emission of the electron.

88
    Radium ———— alpha particle ⟶
          226

86
                                      Radon
                                          222

86
    Radon ———— alpha particle ⟶
          222

84
            Polonium
               218

84
    Polonium ———— alpha particle ⟶
            218

82
            Lead
               214

82
    Lead ———— beta particle ⟶
          214

83
            Bismuth
               214

83
    Bismuth ———— beta particle ⟶
            214

84
            Polonium
               214

84
    Polonium ———— alpha particle ⟶
            214

82
            Lead
               210

82
    Lead ———— beta particle ⟶
          210

83
            Bismuth
               210

83
    Bismuth ———— beta particle ⟶
            210

84
            Polonium
               210

84
    Polonium ———— alpha particle ⟶
            210

82
            Lead
               206

Lead-206 is stable, and the series is at its end. All the atoms formed from the original radium atom are radioactive until the formation of lead-206.

There are over 100 different kinds of elements on earth. An atom is the smallest part of an element which still retains the properties of that element. These 100 elements exist alone, or else they combine with other elements to form everything in the world. If it is difficult to accept the fact that only 100 elements and various combinations of these elements make up all things, one might remember that there are only 26 letters in our English alphabet, and yet combinations of these 26 letters make up all the words in our dictionaries.

Physical Halflife

Not all radioactive elements emit the same amount of radiation. The rate at which radioactive elements decay is called its physical "halflife." Just what does halflife mean?

Scientists cannot take a radioactive atom and predict the exact time that particular atom will shoot out its particle. A pound of radium is made up of billions and billions of atoms. The average behavior of these billions of atoms can be predicted. A life-insurance company cannot predict how long a particular man will live. But with a group of 20,000 men, it can predict approximately how many men will be alive a year from now, two years from now, and so on. In the same way, scientists do not know which particular atoms will break apart and emit rays, but they do know approximately how many such atoms will have decayed in a certain length of time.

As a radioactive substance decays, its activity decreases. As an example, let us say the substance gives off 1,000 particles per second. After a period of time it may give off 900 particles per second. After a longer period of time it would give off only 600 particles per second. Eventually, the radioactive substance would give off only 500 particles per second. This would be one-half as many particles that the radioactive substance was giving off at first. The period of time it takes a radioactive substance to cut its activity in half is called that particular element's physical halflife.

The Halflife of Radium

Scientists have determined the physical halflives of radioactive elements. The halflife of radium is 1,600 years. This means that at the end of 1,600 years, one-half of a pound of radium will have emitted its particles. After 1,600 years, instead of having one pound of radium, there will be only one-half pound of radium.

The unique feature is that the one-half pound of radium left does not decay completely in its second halflife. Only one-half of the one-half pound does. After 1,600 more years, one-half of the one-half pound of radium will have decayed, so that at the end of 3,200 years, one-fourth pound of the original pound of radium will be left.

Why doesn't radioactivity deal in wholelife instead of halflife? The answer is that half of the remaining radium, no matter how small it might be, will decay every 1,600 years. Theoretically, the substance never completely loses all of its radioactivity. Halflife never comes to an end.

The halflife is different for each radioactive element. Some substances decay very slowly. This means their activity decreases very slowly, and their halflife is very long. The halflife of uranium is four and one-half billion years. Some substances decay very rapidly. Their halflife may be days, hours, seconds, or fractions of seconds. The physical halflife of radioactive iodine is fourteen days.

4

Natural Radioactivity

SOME PEOPLE THINK that radiation is produced only by x-rays and nuclear explosions. This idea is wrong. Natural radioactivity has been with us since the beginning of time.

Cosmic Rays

Cosmic rays continuously shower our earth from space. These rays are mostly protons that have been accelerated to very high speeds in outer space. The cosmic ray protons hit the earth's atmosphere high above the ground. Air atoms are struck by these protons, and the basic particles (electrons, protons, and neutrons) are knocked out of the atom.

One of the particles which travels for a long distance is the neutron. Eventually, many neutrons are captured by the nitrogen atoms in the atmosphere. When a nitrogen atom captures a neutron, it emits a proton and converts to a carbon atom.

A scientist would write the reaction in this form:

$$^{7}_{14}\text{N} + ^{0}_{1}\text{n} \longrightarrow ^{6}_{14}\text{C} + ^{1}_{1}\text{p}$$

N stands for nitrogen, *n* stands for neutron, *C* stands for carbon, and *p* stands for proton.

Carbon-14

Carbon-14 is different from most carbon atoms as it is radioactive. Because cosmic rays produce many neutrons, and because four-fifths of the air is nitrogen, an appreciable amount of carbon-14 is formed at all times. And this process has been going on ever since the earth acquired an atmosphere.

Oxygen makes up about one-fifth of the air. The free carbon-14 atoms quickly unite with oxygen to form carbon dioxide. This radioactive carbon dioxide mixes with the ordinary carbon dioxide already present in the atmosphere. Less than one percent of the air is carbon dioxide. Only a small part of this carbon dioxide is radioactive, but it is enough to be detected.

Plants take carbon dioxide out of the atmosphere and use it to make food. The carbon atom from the carbon dioxide becomes the carbon atom of the plant's tissues. So all plants contain some radioactive carbon. It is found in everything that grows.

U.S. Geological Survey

The most useful samples for carbon-14 age determination are charcoal, wood and shells.

Animals eat the plants and/or eat other animals that have eaten plants. Therefore, all living things contain carbon-14. Once something dies, its intake of carbon-14 stops. Carbon-14, like all radioisotopes, gradually decays. The decay process does not stop after the death of the plant or the animal of which it is a part. Its halflife is about 5,500 years. This means that after 5,500 years, half the carbon-14 will be gone.

If a tree contains 20,000 carbon-14 atoms when it is cut down, it will add no more carbon-14. As time passes, the amount of carbon-14 drops slowly. After the tree has been dead 5,500 years, it will contain only 10,000 carbon-14 atoms. After 11,000 years, it will contain only 5,000 carbon-14 atoms. After 16,500 years, it will contain only 2,500 atoms.

Atomic Calendars

When treasures of the past are unearthed, they are usually found to include something that once lived. Samples of these treasures are then burned to reduce them to pure carbon. The carbon is placed in a chamber which is heavily shielded with steel bricks to keep out cosmic rays. Its radioactivity can then be measured by a Geiger counter.

Isotopes, Inc.

An underground vault where radioactive carbon content of sample is measured.

The age of the treasure is finally established by comparing its radioactivity to the radioactivity of today's "living carbon." It is difficult to calculate the age of anything over 25,000 years old, because such an item has very little carbon-14 left in it. Carbon-14 serves mankind as an atomic calendar.

An art collector was considering the purchase of a statuette that was supposed to be 5,000 years old. Before buying, he had a carbon-14 test run on it. The test proved it had been made in our modern times and was a fake.

Scientists are always looking for better tools. Potassium-40 has a halflife of 1,300,000,000 years. It is a more precise atomic calendar than carbon-14 because of its long halflife. Potassium-40 has its limitations, as it is found only in certain types of rocks. Ancient remains cannot be dated by potassium-40 unless they contain these rocks.

Natural Radiation Exposure

Radioactive carbon would not exist without the bombardment of the cosmic rays. Cosmic rays are a high energy radiation and pass through our bodies constantly. The amount of natural radiation exposure an individual undergoes is determined by the place where he lives. A person living in Denver, Colorado, receives a higher concentration of natural radiation than a resident of New York City, because of the Denver altitude. Denver has 5,000 feet less atmosphere to shield it from the bombardment of space radiation. For the same reason a person making a crosscountry jet flight is exposed to slightly more radioactivity than a person making the trip by train. There is a theory that the mutations which have occurred in the human body are a result of cosmic rays passing through our bodies and affecting our genes.

Natural-occurring radiation can also be found in the earth. In India, in Brazil, and in many places in the United States and the Soviet Union, natural radiation due to thorium, uranium, and radium is at the surface of the soil. Because of these radioactive elements at the surface, exposure to radiation is ten times greater in these areas than in normal areas.

33

The definition of uranium before atomic energy had become a reality was "a worthless metal." Today uranium is like gold. It is actually more plentiful than gold or silver, but it is never found pure in nature.

Pure uranium is a heavy, white metal—heavier even than lead. Rocks containing uranium are found all over the world and are quite common. But the uranium in the rocks is so thinly scattered that it is difficult to extract the metal.

Openpit operation in uranium mining.

When a rock contains a large quantity of a metal, it is called ore. In the United States, rocks which contain a useful amount of uranium ore are found in Utah and in Colorado. Other sources are found in Canada, in the Republic of the Congo in central Africa, and in Australia.

Uranium

Natural uranium consists of three isotopes—uranium-234 (92 protons and 142 neutrons), uranium-235 (92 protons and 143 neutrons), and uranium-238 (92 protons and 146 neutrons).

34

Chemically, the uranium isotopes are identical—they all contain 92 protons. The only difference is their weight due to the various number of neutrons. The amount of uranium-234 found in the ore is so slight that it is not important. Less than one percent of uranium ore is uranium-235, while the rest of the uranium in the ore is made up of uranium-238.

Uranium-238 and uranium-235 are both radioactive, and their halflives are very long. The halflife of uranium-238 is four and one-half billion years. Uranium-235 has a halflife of 700 million years. The difference in the halflives accounts for the fewer uranium-235 atoms compared to the number of uranium-238 atoms. If their halflives were not so long, a supply of uranium would not exist on earth. With no uranium, there would be no atomic age.

Entrance to underground uranium mine.

Natural radiation is very small in amount, and it has been with us since time began. It has never posed a serious threat to life. After all, life on earth has evolved in this radioactive atmosphere. It was not until man, with the explosion of the first atomic bomb, succeeded in concentrating radioactive substances, that radiation has become a threat to us.

5

Development of the Bomb

NATURAL RADIOACTIVITY takes place without any help from man. The discovery of alpha and beta particles made scientists very enthusiastic. They had been looking for a "bullet" to shoot at the nucleus. A pitchfork cannot be used to pick up peas, and the nucleus of the atom cannot be split unless a tool that is scaled down to proper size is used. The alpha and beta particles were

A vessel containing pure water is being bombarded by a beam of alpha particles.

Lawrence Radiation Laboratory, Univ. of California

the proper size to strike the nucleus. Scientists began to experiment with these particles that were being shot out of the nuclei of the radioactive atoms.

Alpha and Beta Bullets

With strong electric magnets the alpha particles and beta particles were steered in a straight path so that they could be aimed toward their tiny target, the nucleus. Not only were scientists using "bullets" that were too small to be seen, but they were trying to strike a "target" that was likewise too small to be seen.

The scientists were disappointed when they found that bombardment of atoms with alpha and beta particles created few nuclear reactions. Remember, the atom is composed of positively charged protons, uncharged neutrons, and orbiting negative charged electrons.

Since unlike charges attract each other, the beta particles with negative charges were pulled toward the nucleus with its positive charges. But a beta particle is an electron and is too light to affect the nucleus.

Since like charges repel each other, the positive protons in the nucleus repelled the positively charged alpha particles and knocked most of the alpha particles off target.

The alpha and beta particles were simply not adequate bullets. But scientists made another discovery. They found that a stream of neutrons was emitted by certain substances after being bombarded with alpha particles.

Neutron Bullets

The stream of neutrons gave the scientists great hope. It is uncharged—neither negative nor positive. It could not be repelled by the orbiting negative electrons or by the positive protons in the atoms. The neutron might be the bullet to hit the nucleus target.

During the 1930's different isotopes were exposed to beams of neutrons. Most of the isotopes absorbed a neutron. As a result, the isotopes became radioactive and eventually emitted alpha, beta, or gamma radiation.

When a beta particle is emitted, a new atom is produced whose positive charge is increased by one unit. Until the 1930's uranium was the heaviest and last known element with 92 protons in its nucleus. Up to this point scientists had only bombarded the lighter atoms with neutrons. It was decided to bombard uranium. If uranium absorbed a neutron and emitted a beta ray, a new atom with 93 protons in its nucleus would be developed.

Uranium-235 Nucleus Splits

But the scientists were in for a surprise. When one of the uranium atoms absorbed the neutron as the other isotopes had done, the nucleus split. And in its splitting, new and lighter elements were formed.

The uranium atoms that split were uranium-235 atoms. The uranium-238 atoms absorbed the neutrons, but they did not split.

Enrico Fermi

Enrico Fermi, fleeing from Fascism in Italy, brought this knowledge to the United States. Further experimentation proved that when the uranium nucleus split, enormous energy as well as one to three high-speed neutrons were released. This test was the key to a chain reaction.

By the time it was discovered that a uranium nucleus could be split, World War II had begun. Scientists on both sides of the Atlantic Ocean now had the necessary knowledge that could lead to the development of an atomic bomb. It was vital that the Free World win the race to produce the atomic bomb.

Manhattan Project

At this time the Manhattan Project, a secret scientific program of the United States, began. Experts worked day and night to solve the baffling problems of the development of a nuclear fission weapon. The purpose of the Manhattan Project was to achieve nuclear superiority over the enemy.

Experimentation began under the football stands at the University of Chicago. The first atomic reactor, under the direction of Enrico Fermi, was built here. This was the stepping stone that would later lead to the first explosion of an atomic bomb.

Scientists guessed that unless a piece of pure uranium-235 was a certain size, no chain reaction could be sustained. Neutrons released near the edge of a piece of uranium were likely to shoot out into the surrounding air. These neutrons would be lost forever to the uranium and could not result in the splitting of a uranium nucleus.

To build the atomic bomb, Fermi and his co-workers used two "pieces" (Piece X and Piece Y) of uranium-235. Since uranium-235 is unstable, some fission is naturally taking place, and neutrons are flying about.

Piece X or Piece Y did not produce enough neutrons to sustain a chain reaction individually. But when a triggering device forced Piece X into Piece Y, the proper amount of pure uranium-235 automatically resulted in a chain reaction. Within a fraction of a second, the explosion took place.

The First Bomb

An atomic bomb contains an enormous amount of energy in a relatively small package. It is when a large amount of en-

The fireball, 15 seconds after explosion of the first atomic bomb on July 16, 1945, rises into the air above the desert near the town of San Antonio, New Mexico.

ergy is released in a short time and at a tremendous speed, that energy is so fearfully destructive.

Although the atomic bomb was created by the United States, it cannot be claimed as an exclusive homemade product. The combined genius and effort of scientists of the United States, Great Britain, and other scientists who had come to this country to escape persecution in their lands were responsible. It was an international effort.

In August, 1945, when the first atomic bombs were dropped on Japan, the United States demonstrated to the world that it had solved the riddle of the atom. The thousands of deaths which resulted from the dropping of the nuclear bombs on Japan were a wartime tragedy.

The Fusion Process

The sun also makes nuclear energy. In the presence of the immense heat of the sun, four atoms of hydrogen fuse together to form one atom of helium. Each hydrogen atom contains one proton. During this fusion process, two of the four protons convert to neutrons, and enormous energy is released.

40

Atomic scientists felt that there was an even greater supply of energy in atomic fusion. There would also be other advantages in the fusion process. Fusion is the combining of two light nuclei to release energy.

The heat and light given off by the sun are a result of fusion reactions. For fusion to take place, temperatures around 100 million degrees Fahrenheit are required. A high pressure that can compress fuel in the range of tons per square inch is also required. The problem of fusion is to create these conditions in our earthly surroundings.

Only in an environment similar to the sun can fusion occur. The fission bomb creates the heat of a little sun to duplicate

Rising atom bomb cloud after the bombing of Nagasaki, Japan.

these high temperatures. In other words, the fission bomb can serve as a "trigger" for the fusion bomb.

Since protons have positive electrical charges, it is necessary to overcome their natural repelling action before they will fuse. With large degrees of heat the nuclei are forced to move back and forth at such high speeds that when they bump into one another, they fuse.

Joint Task Force One

The cauliflower after cloud, after dumping two million tons of water, which had been sucked up by the underwater explosion, rises.

The repulsion is greater according to the size of the nucleus. A smaller atom will have less charge and, therefore, less repulsion. Hydrogen is preferable because it carries only one positive charge. The forces of repulsion between the hydrogen elements are the smallest possible.

The explosion of a hydrogen bomb is an uncontrolled fusion. But fusion, if it is to serve man, must be controlled. No small-scale fusion reactors have so far been successfully constructed. One of the problems is that no container can hold the fuel at such high temperatures without itself turning to vapors.

Fusion Versus Fission

Controlled fusion reactions are preferable to controlled fission reactions. Why? The fuel for fusion, hydrogen, is abundant, and is cheaper than the fuel, uranium, for fission. Fusion of light nuclei are a much cleaner source of energy than the fission of heavier nuclei. "Ashes" of fission are highly radioactive, while the "ashes" (helium atoms) of fusion are not.

Controlled fusion has not yet been successful because of the necessity to use a fission bomb to reach the extreme temperature for fusion to take place. It is not possible to control the energy produced by a hydrogen bomb explosion.

Deadly radiation is produced by an explosion or in a nuclear reactor. At present, all bombs are "dirty" because they depend on fission, and they release enormous quantities of fission products. The "clean" bomb is one that would not produce radioactive products. Even if a hydrogen bomb did not have to be set off by a fission bomb, it would not really be clean, for during the explosion there would be large amounts of carbon-14 formed. The metal container of the bomb would become radioactive due to the fast and slow neutrons released.

To the older generations the atomic age is something new. Only a little over twenty years ago, the public became aware of the awesome power of the atom. The first large-scale use of atomic energy was in the bomb. Scientists worked around the clock at the beginning of World War II until they produced the bombs which were dropped on the Japanese cities of Nagasaki and Hiroshima. Historical facts of World War II remind us of how successful the bombs were. The atomic bomb ended the war.

One of 157 fuel assemblies being lowered into the core of the reactor.

6

Nuclear Reactors

ON DECEMBER 2, 1942, the first nuclear chain reaction occurred at 3:25 P.M. Without this conquest of nature, scientists would not have been able to understand the necessary fundamentals which led to the awesome powers of the bomb. After witnessing these destructive powers, man knew he must use the atom to accomplish constructive goals.

Man has turned to the reactor to give us power. An atomic reactor is a device for not only starting but also for controlling a fission chain reaction.

Reactor Fuel

One of the necessary ingredients of a reactor is fuel. The only fuel which can be used is a fissionable material. A fissionable material is one that splits when struck by a neutron. There is only one natural-occurring isotope that splits when struck by a neutron—uranium-235.

Uranium-238 is called a "fertile" material. A fertile material is one that can be converted into fissionable materials. When uranium-238 absorbs a neutron, it becomes uranium-239 (92 protons and 147 neutrons). Within a matter of a few minutes it emits a beta particle and becomes neptunium-239 (93 protons and 146 neutrons). Neptunium-239 emits another beta ray and becomes plutonium-239 (94 protons and 145 neutrons). Plutonium-239 is also a fissionable material. When plutonium-239 absorbs a neutron, its nucleus also splits. Plutonium-239 is a manmade fissionable material and can be used as nuclear fuel.

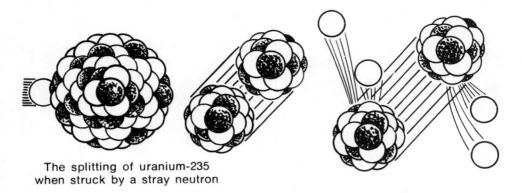

The splitting of uranium-235
when struck by a stray neutron

When uranium-235 atoms split into two parts, neutrons and energy are released at the same time. If a released neutron hits another uranium-235 nucleus, it will also split, and more neutrons are released. These excess neutrons cause more atoms to fission, and a chain reaction is sustained. This process goes on until the fuel is diminished or the neutrons are stopped.

What happens inside a solid piece of uranium? Neutrons shoot into the atom at unimaginable speeds. The neutrons do not aim themselves. They may travel through many, many atoms before colliding with a nucleus which initiates the fission process.

If every fission does not cause a new fission, the reaction will not continue. Atomic scientists call this subcritical reaction.

Critical Fission

If each fission causes a new fission, the reaction is said to be critical. A critical reaction is one which keeps going by itself. It is what actually takes place in a nuclear reactor. In the nuclear reactor the reaction is controlled and shielded.

If each fission causes more than one fission, the reaction is called supercritical. This is what happens in an atomic bomb explosion.

Can a large amount of uranium ore become "critical"? It is true that a pile of pure uranium-235 would be dangerous. But uranium ore contains less than one percent (0.7 percent) of uranium-235. The lower the concentration of uranium-235, the less chance for criticality. In a larger amount of uranium ore, the distance between the uranium-235 atoms is greater, and the possibility of a neutron striking a uranium-235 nucleus is less.

It must be remembered that certain conditions are necessary for criticality to occur. A certain amount of uranium-235 must be present. If the amount is too small, the neutrons will escape before they strike the uranium-235 atoms, and the chain reaction will stop. If a large amount of material is used, the neutrons have a greater opportunity to strike the uranium-235 atoms; few neutrons escape, and the chain reaction continues. In some nuclear reactors such small amounts as 1.74 pounds of uranium-235 can be made critical.

Atomic reactor fuel is usually a mixture of fissionable and fertile materials. When the fuel is bombarded with neutrons, atoms of the fissionable materials (uranium-235) are used. But at the same time the fertile materials (uranium-238) form new fissionable atoms. This is called a "breeder" reactor. Breeding describes the conversion of fertile materials (uranium-238) into fissionable materials (plutonium-239).

Separation of Uranium Isotopes

The ideal fuel is five percent uranium-235 atoms and the rest uranium-238. The naturally occurring supply of uranium, remember, has only 0.7 percent uranium-235 atoms. This means that the pure uranium must be enriched with uranium-235 atoms. So the uranium-235 atoms must be separated from the uranium-238 atoms so that an enriched supply can be obtained.

How is this done? Chemically it cannot be done since the uranium isotopes are like identical twins with one weighing slightly more than the other.

If a small, foreign car turns a corner at a high speed, it swerves much more sharply than does a larger, heavier car. By applying this principle, the lighter uranium-235 atoms can be sorted out from the heavier uranium-238 atoms.

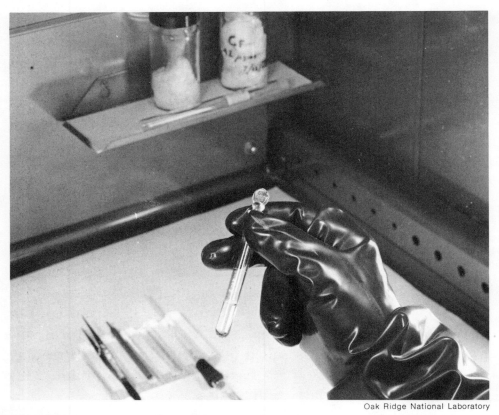

This glass vial contains californium, an element heavier than uranium, which was produced in the isotope reactor.

The uranium atoms are changed to a compound that is a gas. Then the molecules of the uranium gas are given a positive electric charge by knocking off a few of the negative electrons in the outer orbits. The positively charged uranium gas molecules are then pulled by an electrical attraction through a small hole of a powerful magnet. The magnet makes the charged molecules swerve. The heavier uranium-238 gas molecules swerve less than the uranium-235 gas molecules. Two gas beams are formed and collected in separate "bins." This method was one of the first ones used. It separated the uranium isotopes, but it did not produce enough uranium-235 to meet the growing needs.

Another method is now used in the large United States Government plants at Oak Ridge, Tennessee, Paducah, Kentucky, and Portsmouth, Ohio. Out of every 1,000 atoms of uranium, seven atoms are uranium-235. Scientists simply devised an obstacle course for the uranium in the Oak Ridge plant. The obstacles are porous plates that have tiny holes throughout the plates. The lighter molecules (uranium-235) move with slightly greater speed through these tiny holes.

Little boys can climb through fences much more quickly than can their fathers. If an obstacle course with many rail fences were built, and if the competition consisted of 993 men and seven boys, by the time the race was over the seven boys would have finished ahead of the heavier men.

It is necessary to pass the molecules through many thousands of porous plates so that pure uranium-235 is well out in front. This process is much more economical than the separation with the magnets.

This type of installation is called a gaseous diffusion plant. It is in this plant that atomic energy had its beginning with the separation of uranium isotopes. The plant consists of miles and miles of tank rooms, pump rooms, and automatic machinery.

There is no trick to starting a chain reaction. Once you have enough uranium-235, all you have to do is put it together in a lump, and the reaction begins.

Reactor fuel can be in a liquid or a solid state. In the liquid state it is an aqueous solution of enriched uranium. In the solid state the uranium can be in the shape of plates, pellets, pins, etc.

Importance of Slow Neutrons

A uranium-235 atom will absorb a slow neutron much more readily than it will a fast one. The neutrons released during fission are traveling at high speeds. If such a neutron hits a large atom, it bounces off without slowing down. But if the same neutron hits a small atom, it gives up practically all of its kinetic energy to the small atom. As a result of this collision, the neutrons slow down. This loss of speed is very important because slow neutrons rather than fast-moving neutrons trigger fission reactions.

The products formed during fission also readily absorb neutrons. And if many collisions take place, the neutrons might be absorbed by atoms that will not fission. A material that is made up of atoms which will slow down neutrons quickly but which will not absorb them is called a moderator.

What materials are good moderators? Neutrons have approximately the same mass as hydrogen atoms. A collision between a fast neutron and a hydrogen atom results in the neutron losing its energy to the hydrogen atom. Water, acid, and oil contain many hydrogen atoms and are excellent moderators. In some reactors the fuel is spaced with the moderator in between. In other reactors, the fuel and moderators are mixed together.

Neutron Control

How are chain reactions controlled? In order to control a chain reaction, man must have some control over the neutrons which trigger the reaction. This control is accomplished by "poisons." A poison is a substance that absorbs neutrons more readily than a uranium-235 atom will. Cadmium and boron are such substances. Cadmium and boron absorb neutrons, but do not fission as a result of the absorption of the neutrons, as does uranium-235. Because of this characteristic, cadmium and boron rods can be used to control the fission process by inserting them into the reactor.

An uncontrolled chain reaction might be compared to a runaway horse and buggy. The neutrons are running wild and are setting off fission reactions. The control rods are to the reactor what the reins are on the horse. The correct move will bring everything under control.

Usually reactors are equipped with two sets of these rods. One set is for routine control of the chain reaction. The second set is used as safety rods, and will cause a rapid stop of the reactor in case of emergency.

When the fuel is loaded into the reactor, the control and safety rods are in the "in" position. The reaction starts as the safety rods are completely withdrawn and the control rods are

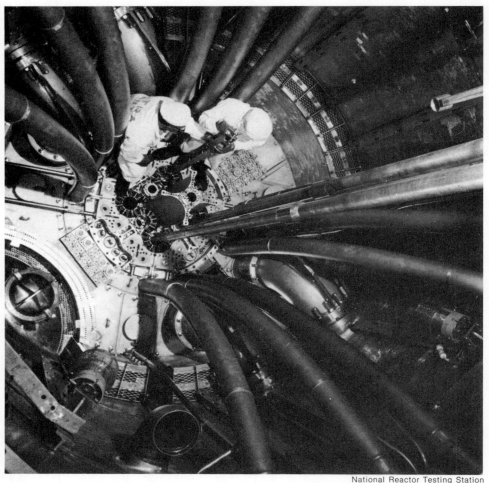

National Reactor Testing Station

Technicians load fuel at the Atomic Energy Commission's National Reactor Testing Station in Idaho.

slowly and partially withdrawn. The withdrawal is gradual and is determined by signals from a neutron-counting instrument which monitors the rate of fission taking place in the reactor. Each atom of fuel releases from one to three neutrons when it undergoes fission. A free neutron exists only about 1/10,000 of a second from the time it is released until the time it is absorbed by a nucleus. If the operator wants to increase the fission, the rods are withdrawn more. If the operator wants to stop the reaction all the control rods are inserted.

As fission continues, there is a loss of reactivity. As fuel is consumed, fission products are formed. These products absorb neutrons and are considered waste. The accumulation of these wastes reduces the reactivity of the fuel. It is like a fire being smothered by its own ashes. To compensate for this, more fuel than is necessary for the critical state is added. This extra fuel is held in check by the control poisons which are slowly removed as fission waste products accumulate.

Reactor Reflectors

Released neutrons will continue in a straight path unless they hit something. A change in direction is sometimes necessary for the neutron to be bounced back into the mass of uranium. This change gives the neutron another chance to be absorbed by uranium-235. The bouncing of neutrons back into the core of the reactor is called reflection. Good moderators are also good reflectors. A container surrounded by water will have more neutrons reflected than a container surrounded by air. Reflectors increase the possibility of a chain reaction.

If two containers of uranium are close enough to each other, neutrons from one can reach and penetrate the other. When the two containers are widely separated, neutrons escaping from one cannot reach the other. If two subcritical containers of uranium are brought close to each other, the pair may become critical since each container gains neutrons from the other. Too many containers too close to each other could produce supercritical reaction.

Power

During the fission process, energy is released in four ways. Eighty-four percent of the energy released is in the kinetic energy of the fission products. Eleven percent of the energy is released in the gradual radioactive decay of the fission products. Two and one-half percent of the energy is released as gamma radiation. The other two and one-half percent energy is released in the kinetic energy of neutrons.

As the fast-moving neutrons and fission products collide with surrounding matter, the kinetic energy is instantly converted to heat. The reaction must be cooled to prevent overheating and melting of the reactor core. Some fluid is pumped throughout the heart of the reactor to carry away the intense heat. The cooling medium can be water, air, helium, or a liquid metal, which must be piped from the reactor to a heat exchanger.

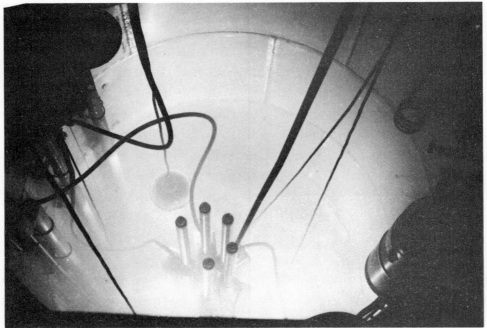

The Martin Company

The entire reactor is immersed in water which serves as the cooling agent, the moderator, and the reflector.

Here it gives up its heat to water to make steam. The cooling medium then returns to the reactor to pick up more heat. The heat carried away is used for power. After all, power is the primary product of a nuclear reactor.

One of the unique features of nuclear reactors is that they are capable of operation at virtually any level. The limiting factor is the rate at which the cooling medium can carry the heat away from the core.

Reactors have different purposes. Some are used to make artificial fissionable material, plutonium. Others are used to make medical and industrial isotopes. Most reactors are used to generate heat power so that it can be converted to electrical energy.

Southern California Edison Co.

The San Onofre Nuclear Generating Station in Southern California has enough power to supply a city of well over half a million population.

Reactor Protection

Reactors must be elaborately shielded to prevent the escape of the deadly radioactive rays and neutrons. The function of the shield is to absorb these rays so that they cannot reach the person or persons working near the reactor.

A typical reactor produces alpha, beta, gamma, and neutron radiation which is deadly to human tissue. A heavy mass of concrete must shield the entire assembly of the reactor. There is an internal shield which consists of a steel lining. Its purpose is to protect the walls of the reactor from radiation damage. The external shield is made of several feet of high density concrete which protects the workers from radiation exposure.

Can a nuclear reactor blow up like an atomic bomb? No. The fuel used could not be made to explode. The principles of a reactor and of a bomb are entirely different. In the case of an atomic bomb, two or more pieces of essentially pure fissionable material are rapidly brought together in a critical state. The fuel is held compressed for a period of time so that a very large explosive force is generated. In the reactor there is nothing to hold the fuel together, so no explosion is capable of taking place.

Albert Einstein

Einstein's Formula

There is no doubt that the energy given off in radioactive releases is many times greater than that involved in ordinary chemical reactions. Where does all this energy come from?

In 1905 Albert Einstein, a young man only twenty-six years old, set down his startling theory. His theory was so new and strange that many scientists did not think it could be true. Einstein suggested to the world of science that the amount of energy that can be obtained from a given amount of mass can be written by a very simple equation: $E = m \times c^2$.

E stands for energy, m stands for mass, and c^2 stands for the speed of light multiplied by itself. The equal sign means that energy is the same as the mass if the mass is multiplied by the speed of light squared.

The formula was the basis for atomic energy. It wasn't until forty years later that the formula explained the enormous energy released from the nucleus of the atom.

The ink required to write your name on a piece of paper weighs about 1/10,000 of a gram.

Steve Walker　　　　　　•　　　　　　(0.0001 grams)

(ink)

The ink is not much mass, is it? Suppose the tiny mass, m, of your signature was totally converted into energy, E.

$E = 0.0001$ grams $\times c^2$ (speed of light)

The speed of light is 186,000 miles per second. The symbol c^2 means 186,000 miles per second multiplied by itself. This gives us a huge number, 35,596,000,000. With this number the small mass will give us enormous energy. It has been estimated that the amount of energy produced could lift a 100,000 ton ocean liner 35 feet into the air!

Hydrogen bomb explosions during the Pacific Tests in 1958.

7

Destructive Nuclear Blasts

THE POWER WHICH CAN BE RELEASED from atoms today could easily destroy our civilization. There are many types of nuclear explosions. A nuclear weapon can be exploded underground, under water, at the surface, or above the surface of the earth. The destructive effects of the bomb depend on the location of the point of the explosion.

Nuclear Weapon Power

Nuclear weapons are similar to conventional weapons insofar as their destructive actions are concerned. But there are several basic differences between nuclear and high-explosive weapons. Nuclear weapons are many thousands or millions of times more powerful than the largest conventional bomb.

About fifty percent of the fission energy in a nuclear bomb is released in the formation of a crater and shock and blast waves. This power of a nuclear explosion is expressed in terms of energy released as compared to the energy released in the explosion of TNT. A one-kiloton nuclear explosion is one which produces the same amount of energy as one kiloton (1000 tons) of TNT.

The sudden release of energy causes an increase of temperature and pressure so that all materials present are converted into hot, compressed gases. These gases immediately expand and create a pressure wave in the surrounding air, water, or earth.

In a surface explosion a large quantity of material is vaporized because of the extremely high temperature. The soil material is displaced due to the pressure and by the rapid expan-

59

sion of the hot gas. The soil is pushed and thrown out, and only a small proportion of the earth falls back into the hole because of the outward motion of the expanding gas.

It has been estimated that the crater formed from an explosion of a one-kiloton nuclear weapon would have a diameter of 130 feet and a depth of 30 feet. The depth of the crater decreases with the increasing height of the point of the explosion. In this area of the explosion there is, of course, complete destruction to any and all structures.

Some energy is produced in the shock (pressure) waves. A shock wave in water or on the ground has the effect of a sudden impact. A shock wave in air is referred to as a "blast" wave because it resembles a strong wind.

After the explosion a series of surface waves move outward somewhat similarly to waves in water. Close to the explosion, rock is crushed by the passage of the pressure waves. The damage due to ground shock will extend as far out as the major displacement of the ground. Underground structures, such as subways, tunnels, and utility pipes are the objects that will undergo the most damage in this area.

The blast wave (air blast) that follows an explosion will affect the buildings that are above ground. The blast wave extends much farther than the shock wave. Door damage, window breakage, and other building damage will be done by these strong winds.

Heat Energy

The second phase of the bomb contains about thirty-five percent of the bomb's energy, which it releases as heat. It would produce burns on people for many miles. The heat rays can kill unprotected people up to ten miles away and cause fires to start even farther away.

Because of the enormous amount of energy released, very high temperatures are attained. These temperatures are estimated to be millions of degrees. Within less than a millionth of a second of the explosion, the extremely hot weapon residue radiates large amounts of energy mostly in the form of invisible x-rays. The x-rays are absorbed by the first few feet of air. This process causes a formation of a hot and luminous spherical mass of air and weapon residue vapors.

This mass is the fireball which is formed after a nuclear explosion. The fireball from a one-megaton nuclear weapon would appear to an observer fifty miles away to be many times more brilliant than the sun at noontime.

The surface temperature of the fireball determines its brightness. It has been found that the surface temperatures of the fireball of a one-megaton bomb do not vary greatly from that of a much higher energy weapon. Therefore, the observed brightness of a fireball is about the same, regardless of the energy released.

Immediately after the fireball's formation, it begins to grow in size. This growth engulfs the surrounding air, thus causing a decrease in temperature. At the same time the fireball rises like a hot-air balloon. Within a minute the fireball has risen roughly 4.5 miles from the point of the explosion.

If a twenty-megaton bomb (twenty million tons of TNT) was exploded, a person would receive second-degree or third-degree burns on all exposed skin if he were within twenty-one miles of the blast. At forty miles away, a reflex glance at the fireball would burn the retina of the eye and blindness could result. After the Marshall Island tests, animals with eye damage were found 345 miles away.

Radiation Produced by Nuclear Weapons

Another threat that a nuclear weapon imposes which a conventional weapon does not impose is the immediate release of highly penetrating and invisible rays. A ground level nuclear explosion not only produces a gigantic fireball and a devastating blast, but it also produces deadly radiation. These rays make up approximately five percent of the total energy released by the nuclear weapon and are referred to as "initial nuclear radiation."

The initial nuclear radiation consists of gamma rays and high-speed neutrons that are emitted within one minute after the explosion. This radiation can travel considerable distances through the air and can produce harmful effects on living things. Although the initial nuclear radiation is a small amount of the total energy released, the deadly rays can cause considerable casualties.

At a distance of one mile from a one-megaton explosion, the initial nuclear radiation would probably prove fatal to most human beings even if they were surrounded by a two-foot shield of concrete. The shield would protect a person from the intense heat but not from the deadly rays.

A large dose of radiation can be delivered to a small part of your body without seriously affecting your general health. But the gamma doses from the bomb cloud will generally be delivered to the whole body. The danger is increased because a person can absorb a fatal dose without feeling anything. A large dose over a long period of time can be survived if your body has the opportunity to repair some of the cell damage, even though there will probably be ten percent permanent damage to the body cells.

The radiation that is emitted later than one minute after the explosion is referred to as "residual nuclear radiation." The substances which remain after a nuclear explosion are radioactive. These substances emit radiation similar to the initial radiation, except that it is extended over a long period of time. This delayed radiation makes up about ten percent of the total energy produced by the bomb.

When a nuclear bomb explodes near the ground, thousands of tons of pulverized soil and rock are sucked high into the air.

Due to the intense heat, a vast amount of earth, as well as weapon residue, is changed to liquid or vapor and is drawn into the sky with the fireball. When this vaporized material cools in the upper air, it condenses back to solid particles. This process is similar to water vapor rising high into the sky and turning to rain or snow when it hits the cold upper air. During the explosion many neutrons are set free and are captured by the many rock and soil particles. Since the nuclei of the atoms have extra neutrons, the particles become radioactive. Radioactive substances are also created by the fissioning of the material of the bomb.

After a bomb bursts, most of the particles fall within a short time because they are heavier than air. They are called "fallout" simply because the particles fall out of the sky. Within twenty-four hours most of the fallout has returned to the earth. But there are other particles which are lighter than air and which drift with the winds for several weeks and finally settle thousands of miles from the explosion. Some of the particles float in the atmosphere for months or even years and are gradually spread all over the world. This fallout then becomes a threat to the entire human population, not merely to the area where the bomb was exploded. The fallout problem continues to be a threat for weeks, months, and years after the explosion because of the late fallout remaining high in the atmosphere. Slowly, the energy is released. Raindrops and snowflakes passing through fallout bring the radioactive dust to earth.

Fallout particles eventually decay and release beta particles, alpha particles, and gamma rays. A person is unaware of this radiation, for it can only be detected by special instruments, such as the Geiger counter.

Body Contamination and Radioisotopes

Radiation of every type is a form of energy. In order for it to act on a living organism, it must be absorbed. Alpha and beta

Research to determine the effects of irradiated soil on cotton plants.

particles are not dangerous when they are outside the body. But if these particles are deposited in the body, they can be very dangerous to specific organs and any living tissue.

At worst, beta particles can produce skin ulcers when they are outside the body. But, if alpha or beta particles should enter the body by eating food or drinking water contaminated with fallout, the sensitive tissues inside your body may be injured due to the constant bombardment of the particles.

The radiation produced by a bomb is quite intense for the first few hours. The major hazard is exposure of the whole body to gamma radiation. By the end of seven hours the intensity of the radiation has decreased to about one-tenth (ten percent) of its amount at one hour after the explosion. At the end of two days, the radioactivity will have decreased to about 1/100th (one percent) of its intensity. About two weeks after the explosion the decrease of activity is to about 1/1000th of its original intensity at the end of one hour after the explosion. The small percentage of activity that remains decreases over a long period of time.

When an atomic explosion takes place, nearly 200 radio-isotopes are formed. A radioisotope is a radioactive isotope of an atom. An isotope is the "identical twin" to the ordinary atom except that it has extra neutrons. Eventually, a radioisotope will decay and shoot out its particles from the nucleus.

Seventy percent of these radioisotopes have physical half-lives of less than one day. The isotopes that decay so rapidly have very little effect on man. The isotopes that have long physical halflives present the hazard.

Two things must be considered about a radioisotope to determine the damage that it is capable of doing to the human body—its physical halflife and its biological halflife.

Biological halflife means the average length of stay of the radioactive element in the body. The biological measure of radiation is based on the amount of energy which is absorbed by living tissue in the body. The more energy that is absorbed, the greater the damage the radiation does to the body cells.

The physical halflife certainly plays a role in the biological halflife for it determines the number of particles emitted by the element. For example, atoms of an element that emit ten particles a minute are less dangerous than atoms of an element that emit 100 particles a minute. But if the element has a 70-year physical halflife, it is no threat to the body if the body eliminates the radioactive element in a short length of time.

Strontium-90 is one example of a dangerous radioactive isotope. It lodges in the bones of the body, and some of it may not be eliminated from the body during the person's lifetime.

Food Chain and Contamination

Green plants are the only form of life that can make their own food. Food is a necessity to provide energy for all living things. Most animals get their food by eating plants. Many animals get their food by eating other animals. Some animals eat both plants and animals. Man is one of these.

A plant-animal community can be broken down into separate food chains. A food chain is a chain of living things directly linked to one another by what they eat. The first link in a food chain is always a green plant. An example of one of the food chains of man might be: grass to cow (roast beef) to man.

The plants at the bottom of the food chain are in a much greater number than the animals at the top of the food chain. If a diagram of a food chain were made, it would resemble a pyramid. At the base would be hundreds of green plants. Above the green plants would be many cows, fewer in number than the plants but larger in size. At the top of the pyramid is man—very small in number. During man's lifetime he will consume many steaks and much roast beef.

A contaminated plant in the food chain could result in radioactive elements in the human body. Radioactive materials from fallout reach the human population primarily in food. Radioactive fallout can stick to the leaves, fruits, and seeds of plants and can contaminate the surface of the plants. Or these "hot" materials can be washed down by the rain from the air and can be absorbed by the roots of plants. Either way, if you eat these plants, you are allowing radioactivity to get inside your body. If you should eat an animal, such as a cow that has eaten contaminated grass, the cow has collected contamination in her body. It will then appear in the milk you drink and in the beef you eat.

Unfortunately for us, the concentration of the contamination is greater in man than in the original contaminated plant. Why? The food pyramid principle applies here. A cow doesn't eat only one kind of plant for food. She eats hundreds of plants. If all the plants have contamination, the concentration is greater in the cow than in one plant. As the food chain progresses, man does not eat one cow. Over a period of time he will eat many cows, and the contamination becomes more concentrated.

If radioactivity is present, it will probably find its way into your body through the food you eat, the water you drink, or the air you breathe. Radiation contamination is never beneficial to the human body and should be avoided if at all possible.

Your body becomes contaminated only because you allow the fallout particles to get inside your body. Radiation does not affect water unless the radioactive particles become part of the water. Then the water is as dangerous as the contaminated food because this is another path through which the radiation can enter your body. There is no doubt in our minds that serious biological effects may be produced when radioactive materials enter the body.

Iodine-131

Some of the radioisotopes produced by an atomic explosion are more hazardous than others. Iodine-131 is a radioactive element that produces the greatest radiation threat within a very short time after the explosion. Iodine-131 is simply the "twin" of an ordinary iodine atom except that it has extra neutrons in its nucleus and eventually emits beta rays.

Produced in very large amounts as by an atomic blast, iodine-131 has a physical halflife of fourteen days. As long as iodine-131 does not enter the body, it is not dangerous. The iodine-131 that would be produced by an explosion would be no threat after a period of one or two months because of its short halflife. But because there is such an enormous quantity produced, and because it is so powerful during the first month or two, precautions must be taken by living things against intake.

Radioactive iodine is deposited from the atmosphere on the surface of plants. Cattle eat the plants and when man drinks cow's milk, the iodine is transferred to the body. Children are much more susceptible to radioactive iodine because they are growing and drink more milk than do adults.

Man also consumes iodine-131 when he eats fruits and vegetables, but the amount is very small compared to the iodine contamination acquired from milk. Most surface contamination on fresh fruits and vegetables can be removed simply by washing or skinning the fruit or vegetables before eating.

The main reason iodine-131 is such a threat is because, once it is within the body, it deposits in a small gland—the thyroid. Your thyroid gland is a ductless gland located in the neck. It is a vital gland because it helps to control growth and also regulates the burning of food in the body. Iodine is necessary for normal functioning of the thyroid gland. If a small amount of radioactive iodine concentrates in this gland, severe damage could result in the cells of the thyroid gland. Defective cells would make a defective gland, and would, in turn, affect your entire body.

There are steps which can be taken to safeguard against iodine-131 if we know of contamination. Cattle can be fed on feed that has been in storage and that has not been exposed to iodine-131. This is preferable to allowing the cattle to range and feed in contaminated pastures.

If children were fed evaporated or powdered milk so that they would not need to drink the contaminated milk, the radioactive iodine could not enter the body, and the threat to the thyroid gland would be prevented. The children also would be fed excessive stable iodine so that the iodine-131 would be eliminated from the body. The important thing is to prevent the radioactive iodine from depositing in the thyroid gland.

A scientist measures the radioactivity of wheat plants that were grown on strontium-90 contaminated soil to study the uptake of strontium-90.

Strontium-90

The most dreaded of the radioisotopes is strontium-90 because it has a physical halflife of 28 years and a biological halflife of 17 years.

Since strontium-90 is a beta emitter, it is not serious to the human body unless it gets inside the body. However, it is especially dangerous once it is in the body because it is a bone seeker. Strontium-90 becomes fixed in the bones of the body and remains there for many years.

Radioactive strontium is very similar to calcium. Calcium is essential to the formation of bones and teeth. Calcium compounds enter the body through food and are carried to the bone tissue by the blood. This process occurs throughout childhood. Milk is the ideal source for bones to receive their proper supply of calcium compounds.

Since strontium-90 is first cousin to calcium, it reaches man the same way calcium reaches man—from the soil. However, fortunately for us, studies have shown that calcium is preferable to strontium-90 in every step of the food chain from the plants to the human bone. This provides a partial biological barrier to strontium-90.

Eighty percent of all strontium-90 is expelled from the body in a short length of time. But the remaining twenty percent stays in the body (actually the bone) for years, and constantly emits beta rays. The damage done by these rays might result in incurable diseases, such as leukemia or bone cancer.

Cancer is one of our most dreaded diseases. All human life begins as a single cell, and through cell division becomes a complete organism. Sometimes cells in our bodies turn traitor and begin to divide abnormally. The tissue grows large, and these cancerous cells grow at the expense of the normal cells. If the "wild" division of the cells is not stopped, death will result.

It is the job of the red blood cell to pick up oxygen in the lungs and to carry it to the rest of the body. The life of the red blood cell is hectic and short. After about three or four months, the red blood cells fall apart and must be replaced by new ones.

The bone marrow manufactures red blood cells and sends these into the bloodstream. The radiation from strontium-90 bombarding the cells of the marrow could result in a malfunctioning marrow.

Leukemia is a form of cancer in which the white blood cells begin to multiply abnormally. They overrun the normal red and white blood cells, and death eventually results.

When body cells are exposed to uncontrolled radiation,

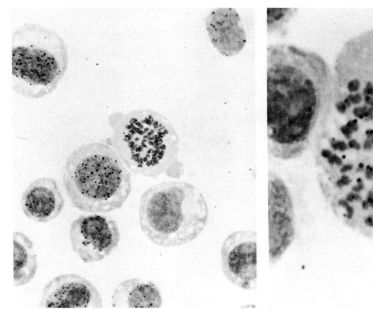

Radioautographs of tumor cells. Left, normal blood cells and tumor cells. Right, magnification of the tumor cell.

there is an increase in cancerous diseases.

Food and water, themselves, do not become contaminated by the bombardment of radiation. They become contaminated only because they contain fallout particles.

Exposed food which has radioactive strontium on it can be made safe by washing, brushing, or peeling the food. To do this removes the fallout particles, and the food is no longer contaminated.

Medical science has recently discovered that aluminum phosphate gel stops absorption of strontium-90 by as much as eighty-seven percent. Aluminum phosphate gel is an antacid which is used by people with ulcers as a stomach soother. This gel can be a good defense if one knows strontium-90 is present, for the strontium-90 will bind itself to the aluminum phosphate and will not be digested by the body. Thus, it is eliminated as waste by the body. This gel must be taken immediately after the intake of strontium-90 or it will not be effective.

Cesium-137

Calcium and potassium are two essential elements absorbed by plant roots from the soil, which are necessary for healthy plants. Another radioisotope, cesium-137, resembles potassium the same as strontium-90 resembles calcium.

Potassium compounds taken from the soil by plant roots provide potassium for the body which is essential for growth. Unfortunately, the body readily prefers cesium to potassium so that, if the radioactive cesium is present, it lodges readily in the body.

Cesium-137 has a physical halflife of 30 years, but its biological halflife is only 70 days. Even though it has only a short stay in the body, it can be a serious hazard to the body because it emits the penetrating gamma rays. It is not considered so hazardous as strontium-90 because of its short stay in the body and because it does not concentrate in any single tissue but is distributed throughout the body. For this reason cesium-137 does not present the cancer threat that strontium-90 does.

Most of cesium-137 reaches the human through milk. Approximately one-fourth of cesium-137 is deposited in the body through meat. Only a small percentage of cesium-137 reaches us through eating flour, cereal, vegetables, and citrus fruits.

Cesium-137, because of its general distribution throughout the body and its penetrating radiation (gamma rays), is most dangerous to the genes. Genes are located in the nucleus of each cell and are responsible for a person's heredity. Genes are the factors responsible for the development of the individual traits of living things. In man there are genes for the color of the eyes, for normal blood clotting, the size of one's feet, the shape of the nose, the color of hair.

When cells divide, the genes in the cells are usually duplicated. But if it is not an exact copy of the original in the reproductive cells, a change will take place in the offspring. This

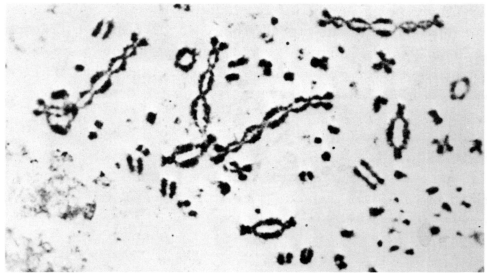

This cell nucleus, enlarged 275 times, has chromosomes that have doubled, tripled, etc., abnormally because of irradiation. Such a cell could easily become cancerous.

change is called a mutation. Most mutations are harmful rather than good. Once genetic change has taken place, it will be passed from one generation to the next.

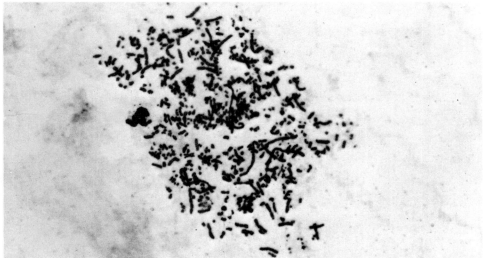

This giant cell nucleus, enlarged 50 times, has grown abnormally due to irradiation. The cell now has more than 700 chromosomes and is about 10 times the size of a normal cell.

Many biologists believe that radiation does genetic damage, but this fact cannot be proved. The reason that there is no sure proof is that the slightest genetic damage cannot be detected for at least three generations. This means that it will be fifty years or more before there might be any evidence of genetic damage.

To some, cesium-137 is the most dreaded aspect of radioactive fallout. It is feared that mental and physical defects might be the heredity of our future generations because of the genetic effect of cesium-137 which we have already received, or might receive, in the event of a nuclear war.

8

Respect for Invisible Rays

THE DANGER OF RADIATION depends on the degree of exposure. Just how dangerous is electricity? or fire? We use electricity and fire every day, but we certainly protect ourselves from both. We are not afraid of them, yet we do not take chances with them. The same should be true of radiation. The more we understand about radiation and fallout, the less we shall fear them. The chances of our receiving an overexposure to radiation is very slight unless there should be a nuclear war.

X-Rays

People have not always been aware of the effects of radiation. The history of x-rays is filled with examples of people misusing radiation. It was some time after the discovery of x-rays (a form of radiation) before man became aware that precautions must be taken. A number of people have lost their lives because of failure to recognize the danger of x-rays and radioactivity.

An accident occurred in 1895, when Professor Wilhelm Roentgen, of Germany, was carrying out an experiment. He passed an electric current through a vacuum tube. A strange glow was being emitted by a piece of cardboard which had been painted with fluorescent chemicals. Roentgen placed his hands between the cardboard and his vacuum tube. To his surprise he could see the bones of his hands. He eventually substituted photographic plates for the fluorescent screen and reported his "new rays" to the world.

Wilhelm Roentgen

The reaction of the world to the "new rays" was varied. Some people thought the rays were amazing and fascinating. Others thought they were indecent. After all, the rays made it possible to see into the human body.

Thomas A. Edison set up an exhibit in 1896 in New York City so that people could see the bones of their bodies and could witness the marvels of the x-rays. When people were reluctant to use the machine, Mr. Dally, an assistant, gladly obliged by exposing his body to x-rays. The overexposure was too much. He died in 1905.

The new discovery brought absurd products to the market. X-ray tubes were sold. Fortunately for the buyers, the tubes were of low voltage. One merchant advertised x-ray-proof underclothing for the prying eyes of people using x-ray binoculars.

One man in Chicago began to manufacture x-ray tubes. He was later treated for x-ray burns, and he eventually had to have his hands amputated.

A professor at Temple University, in Philadelphia, thought his secretary was rather attractive, except for an excessive growth of hair on her arms. He suggested that x-rays might possibly remove the hair from her arms. He was right, of course. The x-rays did remove the hair, but it also left bad burns on her arms. Eventually her arms had to be amputated.

By 1911, much information was published which suggested the hazards of x-ray exposure. Many people had lost limbs and some had died. But not everyone took heed; some continued to ignore the warning.

It was not until after World War I that Great Britain took the leadership and established an X-ray and Radium Protection Committee in 1921. This committee gathered data from incidents beginning in 1895. The light began to dawn on the masses when the committee reported a number of noticeable things. Cancerous ulcers formed, bone growth was inhibited, blood cells were changed, and the bone marrow did not function properly when a person had a high exposure of x-ray dosage. It also reported that different body tissues responded differently with the exposure.

The proper use of x-rays is not dangerous. It is in overexposure that the danger lies. For our protection and in order to obtain maximum benefits, x-ray must be used properly.

Discovery of Radioactivity

Henri Becquerel of France had a fluorescent substance that would glow when placed under an ultraviolet light. In 1896, after reading about Roentgen's discovery, Becquerel suspected that the glow occurred because the substance was giving off rays similar to Roentgen's.

Henri Becquerel

Becquerel thought that the light was causing the substance to give off the rays. One day he placed the crystals on some photographic plates. He thought nothing would happen because the photographic plates were well wrapped. For some reason, Becquerel developed the unused plates, anyway. To his amazement there were black patches on the plates where the crystals had been. It was as if the plates had been exposed to light.

After much experimentation, Becquerel discovered that the substance did not lose its power but would expose photographic plates again and again. As long as the substance contained uranium, it continued to expose the photographic plates right through their protective wrappers. The new phenomenon that Becquerel had discovered was "radioactivity." He became so fascinated with his uranium crystals that he carried some in his pants pocket. As a result, he sustained a burn on his leg.

Marie Curie

After Becquerel's discovery, Marie Curie became interested in uranium and radioactivity. She is known for her life's work with radioactive elements. But constant exposure to these elements took its toll, and she died of leukemia in 1934.

Irène, the daughter of Marie Curie, followed in her mother's scientific footsteps. She, like her mother, suffered from overexposure to radiation. However, Irene Curie should have known better and should have taken the precautions which are necessary when working near radioactive materials. She died in March, 1956.

Radium Poisoning

"Cause of death—radium poisoning," read the death certificate. The first reported death was in 1919 at the Berlin Medical Society. It was the death of a 58-year-old female. She had suffered from arthritis and had been treated with injections of thorium-X. Thorium-X is a short-lived isotope of radium. The treatment lasted for sixteen days. Within a month, the woman was dead. She had not died from arthritis. She had died from radiation sickness.

Sodium fluoride is a rat poison. One gram (1/28th of an ounce) of sodium fluoride swallowed by a human results in instant death. The actual dosage of radium that is poisonous is too small to be seen or weighed. As little as one-half millionth of a gram will kill a person if it is swallowed. No, it will not kill at once. Radium takes many, many years. But the continuous bombardment of the bone marrow by the alpha particles causes tissue destruction. The final result is bone cancer or leukemia.

Fortunately, our cells have a remarkable capacity for self-repair. But if the cells are subjected to injury for a long time, they will finally die or else give rise to cancer-producing cells.

For years, even though it was known that x-rays, alpha particles, beta particles, and gamma rays damaged living tissue, that fact seemed to be ignored. Radioactive substances that emitted damaging rays continued to be taken into the body. Between 1915 and 1930, a popular treatment for any and all diseases was radium. Thousands of people drank radium "cocktails."

Soon after World War I, radium poisoning was beginning to appear among the radium watch dial painters of New Jersey. According to a 1955 medical report: A woman, twenty-one years old, worked as a dial painter at the United States Radium Corporation from 1918 to 1919. For the one-year period she licked the brushes in order to apply the radium to the dials. In 1935, sixteen years later, she complained of bone pains, and was treated for arthritis. In 1940 the diagnosis of radium poisoning was made. The woman had completely forgotten about her former occupation as a dial painter. By 1944 bone cancer had developed, and she died in 1945. Her death came twenty-six years after she had been a dial painter.

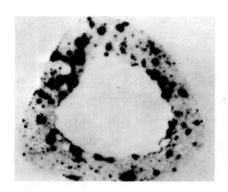 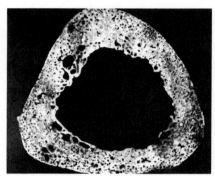

A section of bone from the body of a former radium watch-dial painter, who, in order to maintain a fine brush tip, was in the habit of touching the tip with his tongue. The photograph on the left shows darkened areas of damaging bone. On the right is an auto-radiograph, in which the bone "took its own picture" by being held against film. It shows areas exposed by the radium alpha particles.

Early Exposures and Accidents

But deaths had occurred before Roentgen and his discovery of x-rays and Becquerel and his discovery of radioactivity. In the 1500's it was known that miners in the Erzgebirge mountain range in Bohemia fell ill with a peculiar lung disease. Some of the miners died early in life. In 1878 an investigation showed that the deaths were due to lung cancer.

At the end of the nineteenth century the Joachimsthal mine in Czechoslovakia began to be worked. It was rich in pitchblende, a uranium ore. When the miners opened a rich vein, an accumulation of radioactive radon gas flooded the poorly ventilated shafts. Miners were unaware that they were breathing this radioactive gas. After years of constant exposure, the gas produced acute effects. This radioactivity did damage to the lung tissue and produced cancer in about one percent of the workers each year. Lung cancer eventually claimed the lives of one-third to two-thirds of the miners.

Even though precautions have been taken in recent years, there have been some nuclear reactor accidents. These accidents have been few but they have been dramatic and terrifying.

At the Los Alamos Scientific Laboratory in New Mexico, two accidents occurred in 1945 as a result of uncontrollable chain reactions during experimentations. Ten persons were exposed to high-speed neutrons and gamma rays. One person received an exposure of 2,000 roentgens and was dead nine days later. Another was exposed to 600 roentgens and died twenty-six days later. The other eight people who had been exposed recovered, but after three years had passed, one developed cataracts in both eyes.

The worst accident took place at Los Alamos on December 30, 1958. Through an error, too much plutonium was put into the reactor. When an electric stirring device was turned on, there was suddenly a "blue flash." The man who turned on the stirrer was standing on a low ladder, and he ran out of the building with cries of pain that he was "burning up." His skin reddened immediately, and within a few minutes he began to vomit and to discharge a watery diarrhea. Thirty-six hours later he was dead.

An autopsy showed that his heart muscles were destroyed. His chest was the part of the body which received the highest dose of body radiation that has ever been studied in the human being.

The years of experience with x-rays and radium, the accidents that have occurred in atomic energy plants, and the many experiments with animals have helped scientists to make judgments on the amount of radiation our bodies can withstand. Today there is no excuse for carelessness. We know precautions must be taken.

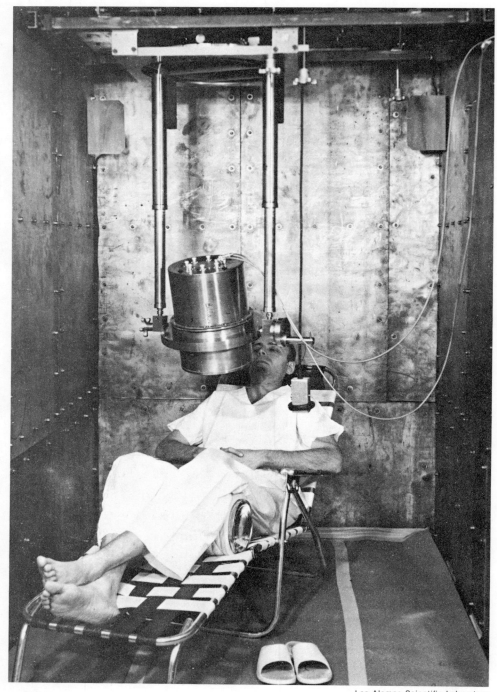

A crystal whole body counter "iron room" in use.

9

Peaceful Applications

GREAT ADVANCES TOWARD THE PEACEFUL APPLICATION of the atom have been predicted for the future. The first steps have already been taken. What are some of these applications that are already affecting us today?

In our daily lives, most of us are introduced to x-rays at the office of a doctor or a dentist. Abscesses at the roots of teeth, a safety pin in a baby's stomach, or a bullet lodged in a splintered bone can be detected with x-rays.

When your chest is x-rayed, you receive approximately one roentgen. This is not considered by the medical profession to be harmful. During an examination of the stomach or the intestine, patients sometimes receive a series of exposures over a period of a few hours that will total as high as fifteen or twenty roentgens. This is also a very low exposure.

Cancer Treatment

High x-ray exposure which destroys body cells becomes deadly when the body cannot replace these cells. But these same x-rays have a place in the treatment of cancer tumors. A tumor is a new growth of cells that serves no purpose in the body. If the growth stops in one place, it is called a benign tumor, and it does not usually endanger one's health or life. But if the new cells show a tendency to spread to other parts of the body, the tumor is cancerous, and is said to be malignant.

The action of x-rays on living cells is quite destructive. However, young and growing cells die more quickly when exposed. Since cancerous cells are usually young and are growing

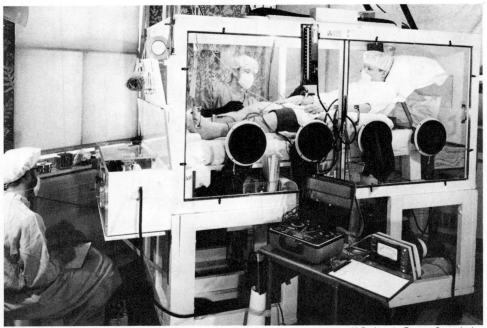

Internal radiation procedure used to treat patient with acute lymphatic leukemia.

much more rapidly than normal ones, the x-ray exposure can be strong enough so that the cancerous cells are destroyed. But the exposure must be low enough so that the healthy cells are not affected.

Medical and dental x-rays are examples of man-made radiation. Most people also come in contact with television sets and luminous dials on watches or clocks, which are also sources of man-made radiation.

Radioisotopes and Medicine

With the dawn of atomic energy, many new radioisotopes became available to be used for therapy and diagnosis in various diseases. An example might be a diseased thyroid gland. A normal thyroid gland absorbs iodine in the same way that a sponge absorbs water. If the thyroid gland is diseased, the absorption of iodine slows down. Twenty-four hours after a patient has drunk an atomic "cocktail" of radioactive iodine, the doctor

84

can pass a sensitive radiation device near the throat and make a diagnosis.

A patient can swallow a radioactive material (small dosage, of course), and a Geiger counter can be used to pick up its signal. In this way diseases can be diagnosed.

Radioisotopes work for organs deep in the body as well as they do for organs near the surface. A healthy liver absorbs gold-198 as readily as a healthy thyroid gland absorbs iodine-131. By scanning the liver after the injection, the doctor is able to determine the condition of the liver. If there is a tumor, it will absorb no gold-198. By the amount of absorption of gold-198 the doctor determines the size and shape of the tumor.

Normal brain tissues will not absorb the radioisotope, gallium-168. Because certain kinds of damaged brain tissue will absorb gallium-168, doctors can use this radioisotope to check brain tissue.

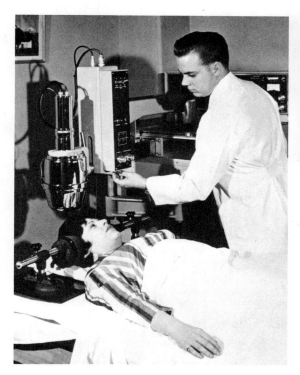

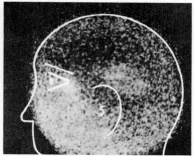

Chicago Wesley Memorial Hospital

A patient, completely comfortable, receiving a brain scan on one of the three scanning devices in the nuclear medicine laboratory of a hospital. The inset picture shows a brain scan made with a positron scintillation camera. A tumor is indicated by light area above ear. (The light area in facial region is caused by uptake in bone.)

Some radioisotopes are given to the patient to kill diseased tissues. The treatment is similar to x-ray treatment, except that the radioisotope treatment is preferred because the selected isotope can be more selective in the tissue it kills.

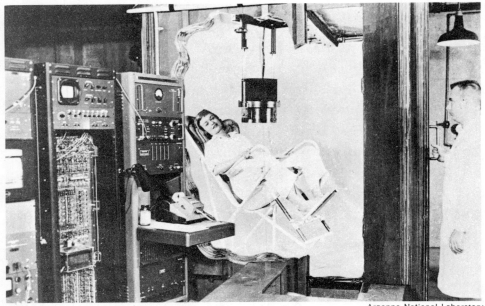

The subject is seated in a chair in an iron-shielded room and under a scintillation detecting crystal.

How is it possible to use x-rays and radioisotopes without doing harm to the human body? There are two factors which apply here. First, the radiation exposure is for a very brief period of time. Second, extreme care and precautions are necessary in using the isotopes and rays. No harm comes to the body because many of the radioisotopes are quickly eliminated from the body. And many of the radioisotopes have short half-lives.

In the case of the radioisotope, cobalt-60, the radiation is confined to a pencil-thin stream which is accurately aimed at the diseased cancerous tissue. It must always be remembered that these isotopes are helpful and yet harmful at the same time.

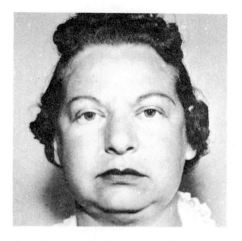

A patient with Cushion's Disease, a pituitary gland disorder, before treatment (left) and 8 months afterwards (right). Five years later she remained apparently free of the disease.

A person who treats people with radiation is called a radiologist. He must be well qualified and expertly trained. It is the action of radiation which gives hope to victims of cancer.

Nuclear energy is not only a marvel in diagnosis and treatment, but it helps man to discover new information concerning the cause and the nature of illness. Nuclear energy will bring about a new fund of knowledge of all parts of the body. This knowledge will give better health for everyone.

Other Uses in Medicine

Radioactivity plays another role in the medical profession. Disease-carrying bacteria can be killed by exposure to nuclear radiation. This process is very important in hospitals, where bedding has to be sterilized (freed from bacteria) before it can safely be used again.

The old method of sterilization was to steam-sterilize. Woolen blankets were ruined by the heat after being steamed three times. By using radiation, blankets can be sterilized as many as twenty times before they have to be discarded. Since there is no rise in temperature, this method is known as cold sterilization. Surgical equipment can be placed in plastic bags and then exposed to radiation. This is a convenient way, for the instruments can actually be sterilized in their containers.

The great source of the atomic age has just recently been tapped in the medical field.

Radioactivity and Its Role in Agriculture

Every minute, thousands of dollars of farm crops in the United States are lost due to insects, plant diseases, and weeds. This loss does not just mean loss of dollars. It also results in people going hungry.

One of the farmer's problems has been the lack of absorption of fertilizers by the plants. Only ten percent of fertilizer spread over a field is absorbed by the soil so that it can nourish the plants. Ninety percent is either trapped in the soil or washed away by rain before it can reach the roots of the plants. The problem was to find out if fertilizer could be applied directly to the leaves.

How could it be determined whether the leaves absorb the fertilizer? Would the fertilizer spread to all parts of the plants if it was absorbed by the leaves? Various fertilizer sprays with radioisotopes could be traced through the plants.

It was discovered that the barks of trees and the leaves will absorb the fertilizer, and as a result, the fertilizer passes through the plant. Today some fruit and vegetable crops are sprayed with fertilizer directly rather than by adding it to the soil.

Plant diseases have always plagued farmers. They have used chemicals to control diseases, but nature has a way to build a resistance to chemicals. The same chemical is only effective for a period of time. Also, chemical control is rather expensive.

By using small quantities of radioisotope tracers on the plant bacteria, farmers can find out how these microbes enter and spread through the plants, how far they are carried by

88

wind or water, how rapidly they multiply, and how various chemicals affect them. Hopefully, this method will lead to the control of many diseases that plague crops.

In the cold areas of the world, frost has always been a threat to crops. Government agencies and private industry are currently looking into the possibility of using the hot waters given off by nuclear reactors to prevent the loss of valuable crops by freezing. In a few years tons of fruit that would have otherwise been lost may be available to a hungry world.

If the weather man issues a frost warning, farmers will be able to protect their crops. Hot water could be flooded or sprayed over the orchards and fields to prevent freezing.

As more and more nuclear reactors pour their excess hot water into the rivers, the temperature of the rivers has been rising. Some of the most valuable food fish, such as trout and salmon, cannot survive in warm waters. If it is feasible to use the hot waters in irrigation, the benefits will be twofold. Not only will the growing season be increased and crop loss due to frost prevented, but our fisheries will be protected, also.

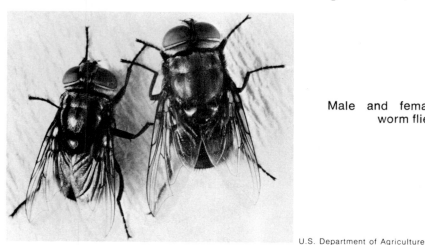

Male and female screw-worm flies.

U.S. Department of Agriculture

Screwworm Flies and Cobalt-60

Radiation is also being used to improve cattle raising by destroying insects which prey on the cattle. One of the most

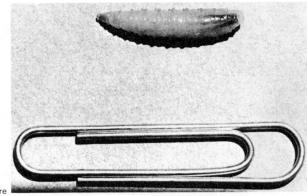

A screwworm larva.

harmful of these pests is the screwworm fly. It lives and feeds on the open wounds of these animals, making them unfit for food—sometimes it even kills them. The screwworm fly deposits its grub on cattle. The grubs, which are immature young, burrow beneath the hides of the cattle.

American scientists conceived a most unusual solution to rid an area infested with these flies. A female screwworm mates only once in her lifetime. If the male were sterile—when they

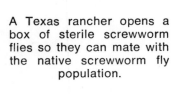

A Texas rancher opens a box of sterile screwworm flies so they can mate with the native screwworm fly population.

mated, no screwworm flies would hatch out—the female could not produce any grubs before she died. The Atomic Energy Commission of the United States hatched a large number of screwworm flies. It then exposed them with radioactive cobalt which caused sterilization. The males could be released in areas which were infested with screwworm flies. The sterile males would mix freely with the normal flies. Each female that mated with the sterile male produced no grubs. As this process was repeated, each generation of screwworms grew fewer and fewer.

In 1962 a campaign began in Southwestern United States to try to rid its livestock of screwworms. It was feared that the pest would spread to other areas in the country. By using sterile screwworm flies, the infested areas have been reduced ninety-nine percent.

This same procedure may be applied to the boll weevil which plagues cotton crops. It may also be applied to the fruit flies in Hawaii which damage the fruits and costs the growers many dollars each year.

Preservation of Food

It has been found that preserving food by irradiation is a better method than any of the other methods used. How could this method affect us? It means that people in California can eat Maine lobster, and perhaps at a reasonable price. It means also that potatoes can remain on a shelf for months without sprouting. Even better, it means that many people who might have died of starvation will live.

The purpose of exposing food to radioactive sources is to kill the bacteria that spoil food. Food has been preserved through the years with other methods. Heating kills bacteria. Freezing makes bacteria lie dormant, and consequently food doesn't spoil. Adding chemicals to food, as in pickling, slows the growth. But these methods make it necessary to cook the foods or to refrigerate them.

Irradiated potatoes, steak, and wheat flour (used in the biscuits are prepared by a chef at Oak Ridge, Tennessee, for a banquet for food specialists.

Radiation works differently. A high dosage of gamma rays is not only deadly to human tissue, but also to any and all living tissue. If a food is exposed to a high dosage of gamma radiation, any bacteria present will be killed. It does not change the food nor does it make it radioactive. Once the food is irradiated, it may be kept for a long time in sealed packages or in cans, without spoiling.

There are different ways to irradiate foods. One is to expose the food to highly radioactive materials, such as the waste products of a fission nuclear reactor. The food is packaged in a concrete cellar above a pool of water containing the radiating source. By remote control, the radioactive cylinder is raised to the surface and allowed to act on the food.

Another method is to use a radiation-generator machine which works on the principle of an x-ray machine. The amount of time required for radiation varies with the nature of the radioactive source. A powerful beam may require only two

Smoked Ham
Gamma Radiation 2.5×10^6 rep
on September 1955
Room Temperature since October 1955

Smoked Ham
Control
Room Temperature since October 1955

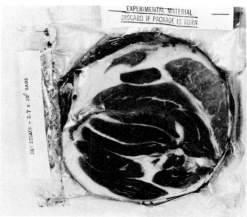
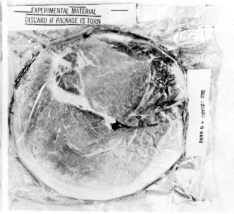

U.S. Army

The smoked ham slice at right was not irradiated, while the other was exposed. After 9 months storage at room temperature, the irradiated slice is fresh and has retained its color. The other one is gray, obviously not fresh.

minutes of exposure, while a low-level beam may take twenty-four hours.

A banana crop produces the same tonnage of edible materials per acre as potatoes, but bananas are subject to quick ripening. The losses in shipment are very great. Sometimes seventy-five percent of the banana crop of a country is lost,

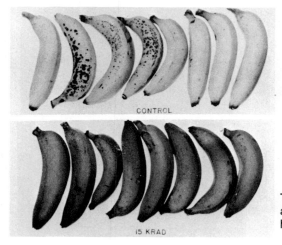

Univ. of California, Berkeley

The two-week-old control bananas were a deep yellow. The irradiated fruit which had been exposed for five minutes was still green with a few touches of yellow.

93

Louisiana State University Laboratories

The preparation of bananas for exposure of gamma radiation by the use of cobalt-60.

due to quick ripening. By exposing bananas to cobalt-60, the ripening of the bananas is delayed, and the shelf life is increased from ten to twenty days.

Not all foods are palatable when sterilized by radiation. In some cases high levels of gamma radiation change the color, the taste, and the textures of the food. These changes are not harmful, but they are not particularly acceptable to the consumer.

The bottom potatoes were exposed to gamma radiation while the top ones were not. The potatoes were stored for 16 months. The irradiated potatoes are still firm, fresh-looking and edible, and without sprouts.

Brookhaven National Laboratory

Sprouting is retarded when potatoes are exposed to radiation by cobalt-60, and potatoes so exposed have been on sale for the past few years in Canada and in Russia. Food preservation by radiation is really new to America, but it will definitely affect us more and more in the future.

For some countries preservation by radiation is a matter of life and death. Why? India, for example, has approximately one-fourth of its imported wheat spoiled each year by insects. The insect eggs lie dormant in the wheat in the cool holds of the ships, but the heat of India causes the eggs to hatch. The wheat lost yearly could feed one million Indians who now starve to death.

The atomic age means better health and more food to mankind. The presence of the peaceful atom is making itself felt more each day.

Argonne National Laboratory—December 20, 1951

The electric light bulbs in this photo show the first known use of electric power from atomic energy.

Small Reactor Power

Today we are already using the energy of atomic reactors to produce electricity. Eventually, most of the electrical power of the United States will come from the mighty atom.

Nuclear powered carrier, USS Enterprise, was launched September 24, 1960.

Nuclear reactors are furnaces which heat water or some other liquid that will drive engines. The prop shafts of ships are driven by a turbine, and turbines, in turn, are driven by a beam of hot steam blasts against their blades. Water under pressure is pumped through a tank, where its heat is used to create steam. The steam, in turn, is directed against the turbine blades and drives the prop shafts.

The submarine Nautilus, first atomic powered ship, on its sea trials.

Atomic submarines can run under water for months without surfacing. The nuclear fuel rods do not have to be replaced as often as regular fuel. Atomic power has not yet been applied to automobiles or airplanes, for the reactors are much too heavy, since they must have a heavy shield so that the deadly radiation will not reach human beings.

A radioisotope-powered swimsuit heater for divers is being tested by the U.S. Navy for deep-sea tests.

An atomic age holds the greatest promise for aviation. The weight of fuel has always limited our flights. Refueling has to take place after a certain number of hours. With an atomic airplane, no refueling would be necessary—at least, the atomic fuel would last longer than would the endurance of the crew of the plane.

Atomic Airplanes are still a thing of the future, for the shielding necessary to protect the crew and passengers from the power reactors would cause excessive weight and would be a detriment to the flight of the plane. Atomic airplanes would work in much the same manner as an ordinary jet. Great quantities of air would be scooped up by the broad intake from the power reactor. The air would then be squeezed by the compression with a specific heat-exchanger that heats the air by atomic energy. The hot air escapes as a stabbing jet at the rear end of the airplane. The recoil of the escaping air pushes the plane forward, as in an ordinary jet plane.

Immense amounts of energy are necessary for space travel. The nuclear rocket engine is simply a compact nuclear reactor.

The power of the reactor rocket engine is twice as strong and three times hotter than any commercial reactors on earth. Nuclear rocket engines are in early developmental stages, but are definitely being used in our space program today.

The high exhaust velocity of the nuclear rocket proves superior to the chemical rockets. The real value of the nuclear rocket is that it produces so much energy, thus making overall propulsion greater. Nuclear propulsion will definitely be the energy used to take us on our long space journeys.

Atomic Blasts for Peaceful Purposes

Can an atomic bomb be used for peaceful purposes? Yes, surprisingly, it has many possibilities. A bomb is simply an explosive, and the use of an explosive has great potential.

A single atomic blast can dig a harbor or flatten a mountain. Whether the explosion is used to benefit man or to destroy him, man must consider the radioactive dust which would be released into the atmosphere.

Atomic fission, unlike fusion, produces many radioactive isotopes. Blasts must be planned so that the radioactivity is trapped in the earth where it causes no harm. Atomic blasting can be a very powerful tool for man. But this powerful tool should be used only if it is absolutely no threat to man.

Valuable minerals that cannot be mined economically might be recovered. A big blast could be used to move the rock covering a rich vein of ore that could not be reached by conventional methods.

The Atomic Energy Commision is sponsoring a "Plowshare Program," aimed at exploring the use of atomic explosions for canal and harbor excavation.

The function of a blast is to lift many tons of earth and to leave a large hole. Experts inform us that ninety-five percent of the radioactive dust is deposited close to a test site. The implication—that a certain percentage of radioactive strontium, cesium, and iodine created is in the cloudburst and is carried to other areas—cannot be avoided.

On July 6, 1962, a 100-kiloton blast showered Utah with vast quantities of radioactive particles. Other than the Marshall Islands in the Pacific Ocean, Utah has probably been exposed to more atomic fallout than any other populated region in the world. This is because it is so near to the atomic testing site of the United States in Nevada.

U.S. Atomic Energy Commission

The 100-kiloton SEDAN event formed the largest excavation ever produced by a single man-made explosion. Note the size of automobiles and structures near the crater rim.

It is agreed by some experts that the testing of nuclear weapons for the defense of our country is a necessity. But these experts question the necessity of allowing radioactive material to endanger human life simply for engineering purposes, such as the "Plowshare Program."

In December, 1967, the explosive power of nuclear energy was used for the first time commercially. The blast, called "Project Gasbuggy," was set off 4,000 feet beneath the earth's surface. It was intended to open a pool of natural gas which man had been unable to tap. A long period of time will be spent evaluating the blast. The gas will be checked to make sure it is not dangerously radioactive when it is used.

Another use of these explosions is to use them as an instantaneous factory of radioisotopes. The number of neutrons released during an atomic explosion is hundreds of times greater than the number of neutrons created by the chain fission reaction in a reactor. The system of making artificial elements is slow in an atomic reactor due to the controlled number of neutrons. This means that the excessive neutrons produced by an explosion causes many radioisotopes to form instantly. These same radioisotopes might take years to produce in a reactor. The explosion is a very effective method for producing radioisotopes of the heavy elements that do not exist in nature. This process has already been demonstrated successfully in underground tests.

How else can underground explosions be useful to man? When an underground explosion takes place, heat is trapped underground for a long period of time. This makes a nuclear furnace which can be put to use.

If water is pumped into a chamber, it immediately turns to steam. The steam can then be used to turn turbines for the generation of electrical power.

Salt water can be pumped into the chamber for conversion to steam. The steam leaves the salt behind, and consequently, fresh water is produced. When the underground chamber has cooled, a follow-up explosion would restore the high temperatures.

Another use of a nuclear explosion is to create caverns which can be used to trap underground water. These caverns could be used as reservoirs to hold subsurface watercourses and runoff from rain. The water in the reservoirs might be tapped to irrigate dry fields.

When dams and roads are built, tremendous amounts of broken rocks and gravel are required. The greatest expense is hauling the rocks to the building sites. Contained explosions near the surface could produce the necessary rock for construction. The cost of the explosion would be significantly smaller than the transportation cost of the rocks from a distant source.

Construction of a sea-level canal would require a series of simultaneous nuclear explosions as simulated in this model.

A nuclear explosion underground vaporizes, or melts, the surrounding rock into a huge cavity in a millionth of a second. This explosion causes the earth-surface to bulge into a huge dome which explodes outward, and which throws debris around the rim of a crater filled with broken rock.

The melted rock far beneath the earth locks in most of the radioactivity, but some escapes into the atmosphere.

Why must nuclear power be considered? Nuclear explosives are very cheap compared to conventional explosives. The same job can be done by nuclear power at approximately one-fifth of the cost of a conventional explosive. When you are dealing in billions of dollars, that is quite a saving.

If the threat of radioactivity exposure can be removed, atomic blasting will make "impossible" jobs possible.

10

Radioactivity and Control

ALL FORMS OF KNOWLEDGE ARE TWO-SIDED. Knowledge can be used for good or for evil. Atomic energy is no exception to the rule. Constructive use of the atom means a happier and better life for all the people of the world. Or, man can choose to use its awesome power for destruction.

Man had to adjust to the Electrical Age, and now man is adjusting to the Atomic Age. Eventually, every phase of our lives will probably be influenced by the atom.

The Atom Has No Loyalties

In the United States each citizen has a vital part to play in the decision reached by the Government about atomic energy. The atom and its potential energy belongs to no one person nor to any one country. It has no loyalties. The atom knows no difference between communism and democracy.

Fallout from an explosion is not deposited on one country. It goes with the wind. An atomic bomb blast puts a certain amount of fallout in the atmosphere which affects all the people of the world.

If we, as a world, concentrate on the peaceful application of the atom, our accomplishments will exceed any of our dreams. But if we must always look over our shoulders, fearing an atomic war, the atomic wonders of tomorrow will be, instead, the production of more bombs. And if these bombs are used, mankind may not survive.

The danger lies in the increasing amount of radioactive materials that man has been adding to the surface of the earth.

Each man, woman, and child on this planet became a "guinea pig" in 1945, when the first atomic bomb was exploded, whether he wanted to or not.

The Marshall Islands came to world attention as battlefields (1942-1945). A beached World War II freighter slowly rusts in pounding surf.

Nuclear Testing Grounds—Pacific Ocean

In 1946 the thirty-six coral islands which formed a ring around a broad lagoon in the west-central Pacific Ocean were selected by the United States to be its nuclear testing grounds. The Bikini Island was the largest of the thirty-six islands and was heavily cultivated with coconut plantations. The coconut provided food, fuel, and building material, and was the only crop that also provided an income on the island. Approximately 160 natives lived comfortably on Bikini.

Because of the nuclear testing, the Bikini natives had to be moved, and they were resettled on another Marshall Island, Kili. Kili had only one-tenth the land area that Bikini had, and there was little protection from the high seas for the natives' outrigger palm log canoes. The lagoon lacked the calm, shallow water of Bikini so that the fish were not nearly so abundant. The exiled islanders called Kili, "Island of the Hungry People,"

Havoc-producing shock wave sweeps over the target ships and races toward deserted Bikini beach while the mushroom of the atomic bomb writhes upward—July 1, 1946.

and waited for the day when they could return to their home island, Bikini.

Twenty-three nuclear bombs were exploded on Bikini during the late 1940's and 1950's. In 1958 the last of the tests was made. The Atomic Energy Commission made a film in 1964 to show the decline of radiation on Bikini, and it was hoped that eventually the Bikini islanders could return home.

During August, 1968, ten years after the tests had ceased, and twenty-two years after the natives had left their homes, members of a federal survey team and nine former residents of Bikini returned to the island. They found that Bikini is now a place that will no longer support a human population. It is a depressing, barren island that is devoid of any plants necessary for human existence.

Radioactivity will continue to be present for centuries on the island. Radiation has declined on the island to such a point, however, that if the natives were to observe certain safety precautions, they could live safely. The coconut crabs cannot, however, be eaten. Because the crab eats its own shell and because the shell is contaminated with strontium-90, the crab meat is highly radioactive. The natives were told that the crabs would have to be killed.

If the natives should move back today without outside help, they could not survive. The radiation is not the threat. The destruction of the bombs has left the island barren of food. Only a few coconut trees that were the farthest away from the nuclear tests still stand, and these few trees cannot support a human population. All the other trees were destroyed. The blasts from the explosion snapped the tops off the trees, while the heat set the remaining parts of the trees on fire.

Rats are the only land mammals found today at Bikini. No radiation-caused mutations have been found in the rats or in any form of life. Scientists point out, however, that in such a competitive environment as Bikini, any deviation from normal life would probably not survive long enough to be discovered.

Some forms of plant life have survived, while other forms have not. The coconut trees can eventually be restored by man. But there is no doubt that since the bomb tests, Bikini will never be the same. It is hoped that by 1973 the United States will have restored the island so that the Bikinians can return to their homes.

It is hard to make a reliable judgment as to how excess radiation is going to affect us. There is little doubt in the minds of many as to what will happen to us if there is a full-scale atomic war.

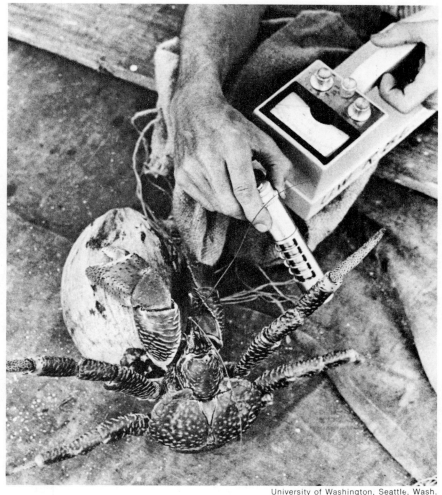

The coconut crab uses radioactive strontium to build its shell. Because these crabs eat their shells after shedding, they are not suitable for food.

Atomic Wastes

As more and more nuclear facilities come into operation, a slight headache is slowly becoming a migraine headache. The safe disposal of the atomic "ashes" left behind by the reactor fuel in the fission process will become a bigger problem. These wastes are lighter elements and are highly radioactive.

Atomic "ashes" may be solid, liquid, or gas. Some have halflives of hundreds of years. Others are less dangerous and have short period halflives. All of the "ashes" can be dangerous if the human body is exposed to them. Atomic wastes are anything contaminated with radioactivity. As well as the reactor ashes, it can be glassware, paper towels, animals used in nuclear experimentation, and so on.

Oak Ridge National Laboratory

Land burial trench at the Oak Ridge National Laboratory reservation. Each day's accumulation of waste containers is buried by 3 or more feet of earth.

The intensely radioactive wastes are packaged in special protective containers. These containers are sealed to prevent leakage and are buried deep in the earth in concrete pits. The concrete walls are at least eight inches thick.

As Atomic plants begin to cover the entire world, high-level wastes will probably be sealed off in salt mines. Experts predict that by the year 2,000, the wastes from atomic reactors in the United States will not take up more than 3,000 acres of salt mines. The important objective must be that these discarded wastes are no threat to human life.

108

The Hidden Threat

An artificial increase in radiation may bring about an increase in leukemia and bone cancer. Shortened life spans and mental defects may result. And the greatest fear of all is the effects of radiation on genetic material in the cells of our bodies.

Young people may be injured more by nuclear radiation than older people, because young people are more apt to absorb radioactive elements into their bones and internal organs than are older people. Since young people are potential parents, they should be protected as much as possible so that the genetic effects are not passed on to their descendants.

Radiation absorbed by the reproduction organs may be carried on down the generations, until its victims become so physically weak that they cannot reproduce, and consequently die without offspring.

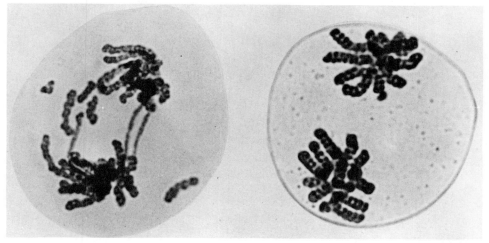

Brookhaven National Laboratory

Effects of radiation on chromosomes. Left, a hormal plant cell showing chromosomes divided into two groups. Right, the same type of cell after x-ray exposure, showing typical abnormalities induced by radiation.

Geneticists are convinced that there is no dose of radiation, no matter how low, that does not produce mutations. The mutations may not appear in this generation, but they *will* appear as surely as the presence of a termite is discovered in old wood.

Information concerning the biological effects of radiation on man is obtained from experimental biology and from observations. In human species, genetic effects are very difficult to evaluate. No experiments can be undertaken.

From the experimentation conducted, it is known that high-energy radiation causes mutations in all living species. No exception has been found. Mice have been found to be about fifteen times as sensitive to radiation as fruit flies. It is true that man differs from other living things in the fact that he possesses the ability to reason. But it is also true that the human's genetic reaction would probably be more similar to mice than to fruit flies.

Studies at the California Institute of Technology experiments produced fruit flies with gene mutations caused by x-ray exposure. A is a normal male; B is a four-winged male with a double thorax; and C and D are three-winged flies with partial double thoraxes.

The genetic threat must always be under consideration by man. For even though genetic damage might show up after three generations, it could be thousands of years before the actual results will be known. At that time it will be too late to do anything about it. For once a gene has been changed, it becomes a part of regular heredity from that time on. It will be too late to have regrets, for our future generations will already have been affected.

Controlling the Hazards

The purpose of radiation control is to limit the hazards. Radioisotopes and x-rays are invaluable tools. The important thing is that we must not suffer from overdoses of radiation due to their use.

Man cannot expect his body to build a resistance to radiation. The only way we can live with it is to master its uses and to control its hazards.

The threshold of the Atomic Age has just been crossed. The destructive truth of the atom was revealed on the deck of the "Lucky Dragon," when the twenty-three fishermen were affected by an explosion which took place over one hundred miles away.

The terrible threat of the bomb lies in the hearts of mankind. It is not the fault of the atom. The threat is man himself.

Atomic energy must be used for peaceful purposes. Eventually, the number of lives saved by atomic energy, through man-made radioisotopes that are used to kill diseased tissues, will surpass the number of lives taken when the massive atomic energy was released on the people of Hiroshima and Nagasaki.

Man and His Creativity

For man's creative mind, there will be no limit to the work the atom can do. Perhaps with the knowledge gained due to tracer experimentation with radioisotopes, we shall learn to duplicate nature's process of food making. Mass production of food by

111

artificial means may make it possible to feed the world's population many times.

Nuclear furnaces which heat water that results in the generation of electricity are already a reality. Each year more and more nuclear power plants are being built to furnish us with electricity to light our homes and to run our appliances.

Air pollution has become a problem to large cities. Nuclear plants are clean sources of power and do not contribute to air pollution. This alone is reason enough for a widespread use of nuclear power.

It is the responsibility of all peoples to keep pace with the development of the atom. We must understand our environment so that we can control our lives and our destinies rather than stumble blindly down the path of self-destruction.

The crux of the atomic problem is human safety. The ultimate outcome lies in the hands of mankind.

Glossary

Alpha Particle—A positively charged particle that is emitted by certain radioactive materials; it is made up of two neutrons and two protons; it is identical with the nucleus of a helium atom.

Atom—The fundamental building blocks of the chemical elements; it contains a dense inner core (the nucleus), with electrons whirling in orbits around the nucleus.

Atomic Bomb—A bomb whose energy comes from the fission of heavy elements, such as uranium or plutonium.

Atomic Number—The number of protons in the nucleus of an atom. Each chemical element has its characteristic atomic number.

Atomic Weight—The mass of an atom relative to other atoms; the atomic weight of any element is approximately equal to the total number of protons and neutrons in its nucleus.

Beam—A stream of nuclear particles going in a single direction.

Benign—Not malignant; a tumor where the growth has stopped.

Beta Particle—A particle emitted from a nucleus during radioactive decay; a negatively charged particle that is identical to an electron. A beta particle may cause skin burns outside the body, and is very harmful if it enters the body.

Biological Halflife—The time required for a man or an animal to eliminate by natural process half the amount of a substance (such as a radioactive material) that has entered the body.

Biological Shield—A mass of absorbing material placed around a reactor to reduce the radiation to a level that is safe for human beings.

Bismuth—The heaviest element (eighty-three protons), which has a nucleus that will not decay spontaneously.

Bone Marrow—The soft tissue in the hollow spaces of the larger bones; it is responsible for the production of red blood cells.

Bone Seeker—A radioisotope that tends to accumulate in the bones when it is inside the body.

Breeder Reactor—A reactor that produces fissionable fuel as well as consuming it.

Calcium—An element necessary to make strong bones in the body.

Cancer—A malignant growth of tissue which tends to spread throughout the body; it is caused by abnormal division of cells.

Canning—Bacteria in food is destroyed by heat after the food is sealed in an airtight container.

Cesium-137—Radioactive cesium, one of the hazardous isotopes formed during a nuclear explosion.

Chain Reaction—A reaction which causes its own repetition.

Charged Particle—An elementary particle which carries a positive or negative charge.

Clean Bomb—A nuclear bomb which produces relatively little fallout.

Cobalt-60—Radioactive cobalt, which is used to treat diseased tissue.

Contamination—The depositing of radioactive material in any place where it may harm persons, spoil experiments, or make products unsuitable for some specific use.

Control Rod—A rod or plate that readily absorbs neutrons used to control a nuclear reaction.

Coolant—A substance circulating through a nuclear reactor to remove or to transfer heat.

Core—The central portion of a nuclear reactor; it contains the fuel elements and usually, the moderator.

Cosmic Rays—Radiation of many sorts but mostly atomic nuclei

114

(protons) with very high energies, originating outside the earth's atmosphere.

Critical—Capable of sustaining a chain reaction.

Decay—The spontaneous transformation of an atom into a different atom; it involves the emission from the nucleus of alpha and beta particles.

Dirty Bomb—A fission bomb, or any other weapon, which would distribute large amounts of radioactive materials.

Disintegration—Radioactive decay.

Drying—Food preservation by lowering the water content of food almost to complete dryness, so that bacteria cannot live in such a medium.

Electron—A fundamental part of an atom having a negative electrical charge and moving in a cloudlike orbit around the nucleus.

Element—One of the 103 known chemical substances that cannot be divided into simpler substances by chemical means; a substance whose atoms all have the same atomic number.

Elementary Particles—The simplest particle of matter and radiation. Examples would be protons, neutrons, and electrons.

Emit—To shoot out.

Energy—Capable of doing work.

Enriched Materials—Material in which the percentages of a given isotope (uranium-235) have been artificially increased so that the percentage of that isotope is higher than that normally found in nature.

Fallout—Particles containing radioactive materials which fall to the ground following a nuclear explosion.

Fertile Material—A material which can be converted into a fissionable material by irradiation in a reactor.

Fireball—The luminous ball of hot gases which forms a few millionths of a second after a nuclear explosion.

Fission—The splitting of a heavy nucleus into two approximately equal parts accompanied by the release of a large amount of energy and generally one or more neutrons.

Fission Products—Nuclei formed by the splitting of heavy elements.

Fissionable Material—Any material that splits when it absorbs slow neutrons.

Food Chain—The pathways by which radioactive material from fallout passes from the first absorbing organism through plants to animals to man.

Freezing—A method of food preservation due to the retarding of bacterial growth for long periods of time.

Fuel—Fissionable material used to produce energy in a reactor.

Fusion—The formation of a heavier nucleus (helium) from two lighter ones (hydrogen) with an abundant release of energy.

Fusion Weapon—An atomic weapon using the energy of nuclear fusion, such as a hydrogen bomb.

Gamma Rays—High energy radiation; these are essentially similar to x-rays but are usually more energetic; they are nuclear in origin.

Gaseous Diffusion—A method of isotopic separation based on the fact that gas atoms or molecules with different masses will diffuse through a porous barrier (or membrane) at different rates.

Geiger Counter—A radiation measuring instrument.

Genes—The bearer of heredity characteristics.

Genetic Effects—Radiation effects that can be transferred from parent to offspring.

Graphite—A pure form of carbon used as a moderator in nuclear reactors.

Halflife—The time in which half the atoms of a particular radioactive substance disintegrates.

H-bomb—A hydrogen bomb.

Hot—Highly radioactive.

116

Hydrogen—The lightest element.

Hydrogen Bomb—A nuclear weapon which derives its energy largely from fusion.

Induced Radioactivity—Radioactivity that is created when substances are bombarded with neutrons, as from a nuclear explosion or in a reactor.

Iodine-131—A radioisotope which is a hazardous threat immediately after an atomic explosion, due to fallout.

Irradiation—Exposure to radiation, as in a nuclear reactor.

Isotope—One of two or more atoms with the same atomic number but with different numbers of neutrons in its nucleus.

Isotope Separation—The process of separating isotopes of an element, as by gaseous diffusion.

Kiloton Energy—The energy of a nuclear explosion which is equivalent to that of an explosion of 1,000 tons of TNT.

Kinetic Energy—Energy due to motion.

Lead—A stable element, not radioactive. It contains eighty-two protons.

Lethal Dose—A dose of radiation sufficient to cause death.

Leukemia—A disease of the blood in which the white blood cells outnumber the red blood cells.

Magnetic Bottle—A magnetic field used to contain a plasma in controlled fusion.

Malignant—A cancerous tumor.

Manhattan Project—The United States War Department Program during World War II, which produced the first atomic bombs.

Mass Number—The sum of the neutrons and protons in a nucleus.

Matter—The substance of which a physical object is composed; anything that has weight or that occupies space.

Megaton Energy—The energy of a nuclear explosion which is equivalent to that of an explosion of one million tons of TNT.

Microorganism—Animals which can be seen only with a microscope. An example is bacteria.

Mutation—A permanent change in the characteristics of an offspring from those of its parents.

Natural Radiation—Background radiation; the radiation in man's natural environment, including cosmic rays and radiation from the radioactive elements which occur in nature.

Natural Uranium—Uranium as found in nature, containing 0.7 percent of uranium-235, 99.3 percent of uranium-238, and a tiny trace of uranium-234.

Neutron—An uncharged particle with a mass slightly greater than that of the proton; it is found in the nucleus of every atom heavier than hydrogen.

Nuclear Explosive—An explosive based on fission or fusion of atomic nuclei.

Nuclear Reaction—A reaction involving a change in an atomic nucleus, such as fission, fusion, neutron capture, or radioactive decay.

Nuclear Reactor—A device in which a fission chain reaction can be started, maintained, and controlled.

Nuclear Rocket—A rocket powered by an engine that obtains energy from a nuclear reactor.

Nucleus—The small, positively charged core of an atom.

Particle—A minute part of matter, such as protons, neutrons, alpha particles, and beta particles.

Physical Halflife—The time in which half the atoms of a particular radioactive substance disintegrate to another nuclear form.

Pitcheblende—A uranium ore.

Plowshare—The Atomic Energy Commission's program of research and development on peaceful uses of nuclear explosives.

Potassium—An element necessary for the growth of plants and animals.

Preservation—The destruction or the inhibiting of the growth of microorganisms so that food will not spoil.

Protection—Provisions to reduce exposure of persons to radiation.

Proton—A particle with a positive electrical charge and a mass approximately 1840 times that of the electron.

Radiation—Nuclear radiation is that emitted from atomic nuclei in various nuclear reactions, including alpha, beta, gamma, and high-speed neutron radiation.

Radiation Accidents—Accidents resulting in the spread of radioactive materials as in the exposure of individuals to radiation.

Radiation Burn—Radiation damage to the skin.

Radiation Damage—General term for the harmful effects of radiation of matter.

Radiation Illness—An acute body disorder which follows exposures to severe doses of radiation.

Radiation Therapy—Treatment of diseases with any type of radiation.

Radioactive Dating—A technique for measuring the age of an object or sample of material by determining the radioactive decay it contains.

Radioactivity—The spontaneous decay of an unstable atomic nucleus.

Radioisotope—A radioactive isotope.

Radium—A radioactive metallic element with atomic number 88.

Radon—A radioactive element; one of the heaviest gases known.

Red Blood Cell—It carries oxygen from the lungs to all parts of the body and returns carbon dioxide from the cells of the body to the lungs so that it will be expelled.

Reflector—A layer of material immediately surrounding a reactor core that scatters back into the core many neutrons which would otherwise escape.

Regulating Rod—A reactor control rod that readily absorbs neutrons so that adjustments of the reactivity can be controlled.

Roentgen Rays—X-rays.

Safety Rod—A standby control rod used to shut down a nuclear reactor rapidly in emergencies.

Shield—A body of material used to reduce the passage of radiation.

Spontaneous Fission—Fission that occurs without an external stimulus.

Stable—Not radioactive; incapable of spontaneous decay.

Stable Isotope—An isotope that does not undergo radioactive decay.

Sterilization—Free from germs.

Strontium-90—A radioisotope that is a bone seeker if it is introduced into the body.

TNT Equivalent—A measure of the energy released in a nuclear explosion expressed in terms of the weight of TNT which would release the same amount of energy when exploded.

Unstable Isotope—A radioisotope; an isotope that undergoes radioactive decay.

Uranium—A radioactive element with the atomic number 92; a white, heavy metal.

Waste—Equipment and materials which are radioactive and for which there is no further use.

White Blood Cell—Colorless cells which take in and destroy harmful substances.

X-rays—Generated by bombarding a metallic target with high-speed electrons; a penetrating form of radiation.

Books for Further Reading

The following books have been especially selected for the reader who wishes to learn more about atomic energy:

ADLER, IRVING. *Inside the Nucleus.* New York: The John Day Company, Inc., 1963.

ALEXANDER, PETER. *Atomic Radiation and Life.* New York: Penguin Books Ltd., 1957.

ANDERSON, WILLIAM R. AND PIZER, VERNON. *Useful Atom.* Cleveland: The World Publishing Company, 1966.

ASIMOV, ISAAC. *Inside the Atom.* New York: Abelard-Schuman Limited, 1958.

ATKINSON, WILLIAM G. *Introduction to Atomic Energy.* New York: John F. Rider Publisher, Inc., 1959.

BARR, DONALD. *How and Why Wonder Book of Atomic Energy.* New York: Grossett & Dunlap, Inc., 1961.

DEAN, GORDON. *Report on the Atom.* New York: Alfred A. Knopf, 1957.

DIETZ, DAVID. *Atomic Science—Bombs and Power.* New York: Dodd, Mead & Co., 1955.

DUNLAP, HENRY A. AND TUCH, HANS N. *Atoms at Your Service.* New York: Harper & Row, Publishers, 1957.

FOWLER, JOHN. *Fallout.* New York: Basic Books, Inc., Publishers, 1960.

HECHT, SELIG. *Explaining the Atom.* New York: The Viking Press, Inc., 1961.

HOGERTON, JOHN F. *Notes on Nuclear Power.* New York: Atomic Industrial Forum, Inc., 1970.

HYDE, MARGARET O. *Atoms Today and Tomorrow.* New York: McGraw-Hill Book Company, 1966.

JUNGK, ROBERT. *Brighter Than a Thousand Suns.* New York: Harcourt, Brace & World, Inc., 1958.

LAPP, RALPH E. *Atoms and People.* New York: Harper & Row, Publishers, 1956.

LAPP, RALPH E. *The Voyage of the Lucky Dragon.* New York: Harper & Row, Publishers, 1958.

LEPRINCE-RINGUET, LOUIS. *Atoms and Men.* Chicago: University of Chicago Press, 1961.

McKOWN, ROBIN. *Fabulous Isotopes.* New York: Holiday House, Inc., 1962.

MARTIN, CHARLES-NOEL. *The Atom: Friend or Foe.* New York: Franklin Watts, Inc., 1962.

POOLE, LYNN, AND GRAY. *Carbon 14.* New York: McGraw-Hill Book Company, Inc., 1961.

PURCELL, JOHN. *Best-Kept Secret: The Story of the Atomic Bomb.* New York: Vanguard Press, Inc., 1963.

REINFELD, FRED. *Uranium and Other Miracle Metals.* New York: Sterling Publishing Co., Inc., 1956.

RENNE, HAROLD S. *How to Detect and Measure Radiation.* Indianapolis: The Bobbs-Merrill Co., Inc., 1963.

RIENOW, ROBERT AND LEONA. *Our New Life with the Atom.* New York: Thomas Y. Crowell Company, 1959.

ROSS, FRANK, JR. *Superpower: The Story of Atomic Energy.* New York: Lothrop, Lee & Shepard Co., Inc., 1960.

SEABORG, GLENN T. AND VALEN, EVANS G. *Elements of the Universe.* New York: E. P. Dutton & Co., 1959.

WENDT, GERALD. *You and the Atom.* New York: Whiteside Inc. and William Morrow & Co., 1956.

WOODBURN, JOHN H. *Radioisotopes.* Philadelphia: J. B. Lippincott Co., 1962.

Index

ABOUT THE AUTHOR

A native of Oklahoma and a graduate of the University of Oklahoma, Ann Stepp now resides in California, where she teaches science to junior high school students in Garden Grove. She holds a Master of Arts degree from Chapman College and is a member of the National Science Teachers Association. Miss Stepp is the author of *Grunion: Fish Out of Water.*

ABOUT THE ARTIST

James E. Barry studied art at the Pratt Institute in Brooklyn and the Art Career School in New York. After serving two years with Army Intelligence in West Berlin, he returned to New York City, where he and his wife now reside. A portrait artist as well as an illustrator, Mr. Barry's books include *Let's Learn About Sugar, The Story of Electricity and Magnetism,* and *A Treasury of Greek Mythology.*